CLAIM INNER H

How to Live a Life with Greater Confidence,
Vitality and Sex Appeal

Kate McKay

Internationally Best-Selling Author of

Claim Your Inner Badass

Copyright © 2022 by Kate McKay

Claim Your Inner Hottie

specialized training and professional judgment of a health care or mental health care professional.

Neither the author nor the publisher can be held responsible for the use of the information provided within this book. Please always consult a trained professional before making any decision regarding treatment of yourself or others.

For inquiries or bulk copies email media@kate-mckay.com.

Paperback ISBN: 979-8-9851259-1-7

Cover and Back Photo: Maya Mauis

Interior Photos: Will Boynton

YOUR FREE GIFT!

CLAIM YOUR INNER BADASS

WORKBOOK

---❖---

KATE MCKAY

Best-Selling Author of
Claim Your Inner Badass

Want to grab a preview copy of Kate's Best Selling Book
Claim Your Inner Badass?

Grab your copy here: https://courses.kate-mckay.com/cyib-workbook

"To remain indifferent to the challenges we face is indefensible. If the goal is noble, whether or not it is realized within our lifetime is largely irrelevant. What we must do therefore is to strive and persevere and never give up." – **Dalai Lama**

"Our very survival (and ultimate success) depends on our ability to stay awake, to adjust to new ideas, to remain vigilant and to face the challenge of change." – **Martin Luther King Jr.**

"My dear friend, clear your mind of can't.

Samuel Johnson

Table of Contents

Introduction

Hello and welcome to the Claim Your Inner Hottie Tribe. Here in the land of Inner Hottie Heaven, we believe that being fit and sexy starts from within.

The Inner Hottie Lifestyle Plan is a holistic approach to health because, as with any transformation, the rebirth begins on the inside. The Inner Hottie lifestyle Plan incorporates mind, body, and spirit for getting fit and feeling your best. You can't make changes in one area without affecting the others.

Holistic:("holos"–whole) of or relating to the consideration of the complete person, physically and psychologically.

As your coach and cheering squad, I am 100% focused on helping, guiding, inspiring and even challenging you to ensure that you reach your goals. I am here to hold your highest vision of health and wellness.

If I see you lose that vision, I will remind you, cajole you, humor you, and challenge you to go all out. Sometimes, I may even irritate you, as I challenge your limiting beliefs. I'm okay with that.

I will not let you settle for less than you deserve or desire. My commitment to YOUR success is that important to me- to inspire you to have the courage and faith to go all out to be your best self and feel amazing.

Kate Flash: As part of the Inner Hottie program, please stay open to shifts in your self-perception. You must be committed to releasing any self-defeating language and behaviors. And most importantly, staying open to living the life your heart desires.

The process is not always easy, but I promise you it will be worth it.

Will you trust me on that?

Please don't sell yourself short. I will do all I can to ensure that your dream becomes your reality.

Beware! Please watch out for these *Hottie Hazards* that could impede your progress throughout the book.

Part 1

The Backstory of The Author's Journey to Claim Her Own Inner Hottie

Chapter 1

The Claim Your Inner Hottie Promise

Are you ready to:

- Live your life all out?
- Unleash your inner hottie?
- Let go of the self sabotaging behaviors and thoughts that have led to living your life way too small?
- Recalibrate the way you think about food so you enjoy nourishing your body?
- Increase your overall vitality and sex appeal?
- Reclaim your inner peace and joy in living?

If you answered a wholehearted "yes!" to the above, congratulations for putting yourself at the center of your breakthrough life.

For those of you who are just hearing about the Inner Hottie Lifestyle Plan, welcome aboard. We're so excited to have you as a part of this Hottie Hoedown!

The Inner Hottie Lifestyle Plan is about redefining and embracing your "sexy"– that part of you that is full of confidence, passion, and celebration.

We embrace that living "fit" means having bodies that reflect our deep and passionate nature. It means living lives of health, wellness, and positive self-acceptance from the inside out.

The Inner Hottie Lifestyle is centered around integrity and grace. The vehicle for these values is a body that's a reflection of your inner peace, joy, and power. It's about turning on high the ole' self-love, because the bottom line is this: without positive self-worth and inner spic mojo, our sex appeal fizzles like a sparkler in a rainstorm.

Mojo: "A charm or a spell. A power that seems magical and allows someone to be very effective or successful, or to have more sex appeal."

Chapter 2

The Proof is in the Pudding –A Lifetime Dedicated to Fitness and Health

I remember the first time I held a weight in my hand. I was a junior at Bennington College – a misfit Irish Catholic Bostonian in a predominantly Jewish New York school. Clove cigarettes filled the air and the preferred wardrobe was black. The incongruity between the beautiful pastoral campus and the school's teeming punk rock kids from Long Island was both humorous and unnerving.

The only way I was able to differentiate myself at a school like this – where I was on a full scholarship and felt like the token "poor kid"– was to become a jock. In the early 1980s there was no gym facility at the school; so, a few of us teamed-up together, got hold of some weight equipment, and converted a small space behind the mailroom into a makeshift gym.

The equipment was old and rusty. I remember lying back on the bench press. As I lifted the weight up off the rack, I felt a nostalgic sensation course through my body. The weight felt good, like a stretch and shock to the system. Somehow it calmed me, making me feel centered and peaceful. My first set left me feeling delightfully dizzy; you could say I was hooked!

After I graduated from Bennington in 1985, I moved back to Boston and became part of the 80s fitness craze. I cut my t-shirts way before *FlashDance* – by the time the movie came out, I thought the Jennifer Beal look was passé. I belonged to a gym called Women's World which was hot pink and flashy. The jiggle machines (where you strapped a belt around your butt, flipped the switch and jiggled your way to fitness) were front and center when you walked into the club. The older ladies hung out there and shimmied and shook with looks of bland disconnect.

It was there that I took my first aerobics class from bleached-blonde girls with hot-pink leg warmers. One instructor reminded me of Barbie – perky, beautiful, and rail thin. We all wanted to be her. A couple of weeks after starting my workout regime at the hot pink club, I distinctly remember sitting in a chair, placing my hands on arms and lifting my legs up with the use of my newfound abs. Wow. It felt amazing!

After being at Women's World for a few months, I grew weary of the club's culture. I visited a coed gym owned by a Russian mother-daughter duo. These women ran the gym like it was the Russian Union; they expected everyone to use strict form and to obey their method of exercise – or they would show you the door. It was here that I met a cute Italian boyfriend who introduced me to the world of Arnold Schwarzenegger and Rachel McLeish, the hottest bodybuilders of the 80s. My boyfriend, Joe, a Sylvester Stallone look-alike, was a dreamboat. He went on a search to find us the perfect gym and one night returned victorious.

Universe Gym had posters of all the past and present bodybuilders plastered on the walls. It was located on the top floor in a dirty old factory in a wasteland in

7

Somerville, Massachusetts. We instantly felt at home. The gym was hardcore; no air conditioning, loud music, hunky men, and – not surprisingly – no girls except for a handful of brave souls. I loved this place- it felt like home.

If I needed the restroom, I had to ask one of the guys to watch the door while I used the only bathroom. They were honored to do it – standing there, ensuring my complete and utter privacy. I felt taken care of, part of a family, and learned everything I needed to know about sculpting the human form. At the gym, this was our seemingly bizarre but completely dedicated art form.

I was busy working as a property manager, exercising and having fun. In fact, I met my husband at a gym in Boston in 1990. We married in 1994. It was a tumultuous marriage, with too many moves and job changes to count. And still the gym remained my sanctuary through the years, despite the chaos of my marriage.

Through the late '90s, I was busy birthing and mothering my three children. Pregnancy was not easy for me, and the morning sickness knocked me to my knees for weeks at a time. But immediately following the birth of my first two kids, I was back at the gym getting in shape, despite the 30 to 35 pounds of pregnancy weight.

However, after my third child, a daughter, in 2001, something shifted for me and I wasn't sure what. I felt uneasy within myself. My anxiety and self-doubt reached critical mass at this time, and I knew that something seriously had to change.

One of the changes I decided to take on was to get my body back. This meant getting my out-of-shape, mommy body to a gym, PRONTO. I hired a trainer. I found a "real gym" in Amesbury, Massachusetts, called Hard Nocks. Does the name describe it for you or what?

Wammo! My Own Personal Transformation.

There is nothing like getting hit by a cosmic 2x4.

Have you ever had a time in your life when everything you believed to be true fell completely by the wayside? You look in your closet and wonder, "Who bought all these clothes?" You look in the mirror and ask, "Who styled this hair-do? Who's body is this?" You look across the breakfast table at your significant other and think, "Who are YOU?"

Well, walking into that gym, post-third child, was THAT time for me. Everything was so crystal clear and completely unrecognizable all at the same time. I was committed to something yet I wasn't clear what it was. All I knew is that there was no turning back.

Personal transformation is just like that. For as much as you want to pretend that everything is just as it was, we both know that once you wake up you can't just pretend to go back to sleep, no matter how hard you try.

And I tried, let me tell you! As sick as it is, I was *seriously, almost comically*, attached to my self-doubt, self-loathing, less-than-stellar relationships, and my life being so whacked and out of balance.

But as the coach and author, Anthony Robbins, describes it – oftentimes, transformation doesn't happen until we **get so disturbed** with a situation that we finally cry "enough!"

What will it take for you to finally take the plunge and be the best version of you?

HOW BAD DO YOU WANT IT?

What is your reason for saying "never mind" just days or moments after committing to making a change, even when you know it is ultimately in your best interest – body, mind, and soul – to lose weight and get fit?

Prior to my new career as a High-Performance Coach and Strategist, I spent more than a decade as a health and fitness coach. I was continually surprised by how the extra pounds "weighed" so heavily on the spirits of my clients. I could see the soul-sucking defeat of not doing what they truly desired. So I would say, "I want more for you, because I see that you want it and you are worthy of that." Instantly, I saw the shift and the commitment was sealed – both mine and theirs.

It is the same process I do in my work as a Coach now-holding the higher vision for my clients, and that includes you, my dear reader.

So you say you are committed. That's awesome to get us started. But the fact is, we need concrete steps to attain all that we desire. Ninety-nine point nine percent of the time, making a big change is a solo mission at the start. Embracing our best selves means we need to stand in and stake a claim for our time, for our vision, for our sense of integrity. And no one can give us that but ourselves. And your dreams are worth it.

You are hot. Isn't it time you claimed it?

When we start the process of transformation it is key that we choose one or two people that we trust that will hold the higher vision for us. There are also plenty of communities out there on social media land to support you. Be brave. Ask for the help you need. The right and perfect people are waiting for you and willing to support you.

I know change is hard, I really do, but it is going to be so worth it.

I am so excited for you to be a part of the Inner Hottie journey. Let's go!

Chapter 3

The Claim Your Inner Hottie Lifestyle Plan

The Inner Hottie Lifestyle takes a holistic approach to getting *and staying* fit. While eating clean and exercise are key elements to the plan, your inner work, or your *Motivational Mojo* (that "something" that makes you tick), is the foundation for rocking your hotness and living the breakthrough life you deserve.

Clean Eats 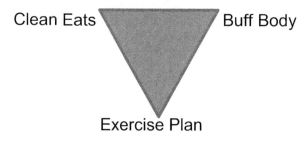 Buff Body

Exercise Plan

Motivational Mojo

What happens on the inside – your emotions, self-talk, patterns and behaviors – have a direct impact on how you look and feel on the outside. That is why we emphasize so strongly the importance of your inner motivation, or your "mojo". This mojo is the inner magic that moves us beyond what we thought we could ever do. It's truly the secret sauce to success.

Transformation is an inside job. Sure, your *will* and *desire* to succeed are important parts, however, truly the most important element of the Inner Hottie program is fully accepting that you are worthy to live your life all out

– and to let your hotness shine like the blazing sun on the Fourth of July.

"You deserve to melt popsicles, Baby!"

Let's Start Claiming Our Inner Hottie Here...

First, let's go over the **Five Components** that make up the Inner Hottie Lifestyle Plan so you can unleash your Inner Hottie with a bang. We will revisit and go deeper with these topics throughout the book so you can fully immerse yourself in the Inner Hottie System. I want you to be ragingly successful, so let's begin:

1. FACE THE TRUTH – Get Real: Face what is. In the Motivational Mojo chapters, we will explore areas in our lives where we have been blowing smoke up our own hineys because we have been too afraid to face the truth. It's time to face the music and accept what IS. Acceptance is the only true path to freedom.

   If you are overweight, out of shape, full of self-loathing and self-doubt, it's time to get real with yourself and face the piper. They are not going anywhere until we muster the courage to stop kidding ourselves and blaming others. I know. It's hard. I've been there. But this time I think you are ready. Can you feel it?

2. RELEASE YOUR BAGGAGE AND LIVE YOUR INNER HOTNESS – It's time to let go. Release what no longer serves your Inner Hottie and step out of the way of your inner sizzle that is ready to be released.

OK, so you faced the music and now you have to figure out what luggage (emotionally speaking) stays and which gets the old heave-ho. Start with people, habits, behaviors, and things. It's amazing how much energy we spend on relationships, emotions, and things well past their expiration dates. Decide if it is worth it to re-up the contract or is it time to switch carriers altogether? Face the fact that for some, it is time for the loving and gentle boot. You are worthy of great things. Dimming your light for anyone or anything is no longer an option at this stage of the game. Move courageously forward.

3. CELEBRATION – Celebrate and Radiate: A big part of the Inner Hottie Lifestyle Plan is celebrating the uniqueness of who we are. These bodies we were given, even with their imperfections and battle wounds, are worth celebrating.

   If we cannot celebrate ourselves, who else will?

   Now is your time to shine and live your amazing breakthrough life. And *that* is cause for celebration. Confidence is *sexy*. To be confident, you have to believe that you can attain your goals and – the best part – knowing that you are worthy of attaining them.

4. CLEAN EATING – Eat Clean: Self-respect begins at the lips, not the hips. It's time to fuel your machine with clean eats. Eating healthy is a commitment to your highest and best self. You are

worthy of self-care. You will feel better. Look better. And people will definitely notice.

Eating well fuels the mind, body and soul. Nutrition is a big piece of the Inner Hottie game. Embracing this principle will give you the body you want and deserve. You'll throw out the junk and fill your trunk with whole foods that nurture that inner goddess. Smoking, Baby!

5. EXERCISE – Move It: Find your Inner Hottie in your pleasure of motion. How does it happen? We get lulled into thinking that the couch and our phone are way more important than moving our bodies freely and celebrating our holiness as gods and goddesses.

   If we don't use it, we will most certainly lose it. The joy we find in moving our bodies reflect our inner beauty. This is a gift that many squander. Through a combination of weight training and cardiovascular exercise, we will crank the furnaces of our Hottie love machines!

Life is a Journey. We don't call the PRESENT the PRESENT for nothing. Unwrap your gifts and DO YOUR DAY, THIS DAY, like nobody's business.

"But, Kate, you have no idea how busy, overworked, depressed, exhausted, broke, tired, sore, I am."

My answer is, "Oh, yes, I do!"

I remember when I was a single mom of three, a bikini fitness competitor, and a multimillion-dollar business owner, and I was literally a HOT MESS on the inside.

Trust me, I totally get that life's challenges – and being perpetually overwhelmed and exhausted – can literally knock us to our knees. Life stress is REAL, and it can weigh us down not only physically, but also emotionally and spiritually. I get it, I really do.

KATE GETS REAL ON HER OWN BREAKDOWN

I remember it clearly- that time in my life when I finally threw up the white flag and surrendered.

I was living a life that felt completely out of control. I *had* to do something. I remember the feelings like it was yesterday, meeting my future trainer, Rick. My self-doubt and self-loathing had reached an all-time high– I no longer felt that my body was mine, my spirit was crushed. "What had happened to the old energetic, vivacious me?" I wondered. I felt like a shell of myself, so filled with sadness and shame.

I had spent my thirties happily giving birth and caring for my babies – my number one priority was to nurture these cuties. However, the process of full-on mothering made me unrecognizable to myself! I remember looking in the mirror one fateful day and shaking my head, wondering, "where did *she*, the free spirit I vaguely remembered, go?" The look in my eyes of utter defeat and desperation begged the question, "How could this have happened?"

At that point, I was so disturbed that taking immediate action became absolutely non-negotiable. My trainer could see the fire in me, even though I barely felt it myself. So, I leaned on his faith, and that, my dear friends, made all the difference.

Can you relate to this story?

Are you experiencing something similar as you look at yourself in the mirror? Are you experiencing this *crazy* incongruity of knowing that the person who is looking back at you, with the bulges and bags, is in NO WAY a true reflection of who you really are and want to be?

Are you hungry and disturbed enough by that image to release the fear and self-loathing necessary to all out EMBRACE the Inner Hottie?

KATE'S BREAKDOWN TO BREAKTHROUGH

I realized at my moment of crisis that staying in this state was 100% no longer acceptable. I was so **disturbed** by how I felt and what I saw that I took immediate and radical action to get my fit and sexy self back, as quickly as possible.

The five steps I took were as follows:

1. I made a commitment to myself to get back in shape. I wanted to be in the best shape of my life at age 43. I went all out to do just that. NO MATTER WHAT.

2. I joined a gym, not a health spa. Hard Nocks had old equipment and the same Godsmack CD on replay. The place was filled with die-hard gym types, often smelly and grunting loudly. I was convinced that my first crush, Rocky, would be stepping through the door at any moment and, hey, I wanted to be ready! Ha!

3. I hired a trainer who saw the "fire" in my eyes and kept me on task. He scared me, and I needed to be scared – trust me! He saw something in me that I didn't. I wanted to understand what that was.

4. I shifted my diet in a big way. More protein, fewer carbs. Food became a fuel and less of a way to soothe myself emotionally.

5. I got my family and friends on board who were ready to support me. Either they're with you as you begin your transformation or they're not. It became really clear, painfully clear, who were my supporters and who were my saboteurs. Was this part easy? Nope. Was it necessary? Hell yeah.

If I can do this, so can you.

Results: Big!

Challenging: Heck yes!

Satisfaction: High!

Goal achieved: You be the judge!

KATE'S BIG TRUTH:

The reason I tell my story is because, behind all the glitz and glamour of the bikini photo above, is a woman who fought like H-E-Double Hockey Sticks to earn my place on that stage, despite my brother's tragic murder, my gut-wrenching divorce, the heart-wrenching loss of my son, and my own soul-sucking personal transformation of a woman enmeshed in so much self-doubt and self-loathing I could have sunk the Titanic. True story.

So this is why, my Inner Hottie gods and goddesses, I am 100% committed to being a part of your success. Because I understand the journey, and there is nothing I am more excited about than your amazing, awe-inspiring, and head-turning transformation.

So, let's begin.

Part 2
The Inner Hottie
Motivational Mojo

Chapter 4

Motivational Mojo: From the Inside Out

Getting to Your "WHY" So You Can Live Your Brilliance

Usually the first response I get when I tell people I am pushing 60 years old is, "No way!" They ask my advice about a new diet pill or other shortcuts they can take to get skinny or get ripped. They want to believe so desperately that there must be a newfangled diet or certain exercise machine out there that will get them sexy and buff lickety-split.

"Well, isn't there?? I read about it online…"

"Saw it on *Facebook, IG, TikTok*…"

"My friend just told me about it…"

When people find out that the key to my success has been simple clean eating and exercise, they are severely disappointed. I can almost hear their inner dialogue saying dejectedly, "That will never be me. I could never do that."

Screech!

And I implore, "Why not?"

Why not YOU? Why not?

Why is it that so many of us resign ourselves to mediocre lifestyles? Why do we settle for the status quo or good enough? The flipside to this question is the real juice:

What does it take to motivate and inspire people who DO succeed in getting their sexy back?

What I have found true for my clients, who have been successful in attaining their fitness and lifestyle goals is what they describe as an *internal* shift that expanded their sense of possibility in themselves. This is what motivated them to take the plunge and make the changes necessary to live a kick-butt life.

This is cool stuff and worth expanding on with greater detail.

Internal vs. External Motivators

Why Does it Matter?

Wouldn't it be great if we could "just do it," as Nike proclaims? Unfortunately, understanding what motivates people to get fit and lose weight often precludes the "just do it" mentality.

People are motivated by all kinds of things: looking more attractive, fitting into a wedding dress, impressing peers, proving to family that they have the willpower to succeed, and so on.

And what do all these things have in common? These are all *extrinsic*, or *external*, motivators that are concerned with how other people perceive us.

And guess what? These external motivators are much less likely to stick. It's not enough to make the shift for someone else – we need to want it for ourselves.

Intrinsic, or internal, motivators are driven by our desire to live more in line with our own values, the essential nature of who we are. I continually ask my clients about their own personal visions – what is it that drives them on a daily basis? Everyone has a unique plan and my job as a coach is to help foster and encourage my clients' dreams. I have the pleasure of watching them unfold.

Internal/Intrinsic Motivators
80% of the motivational game
Taking pleasure in an activity driven by an inner sense of
reward or accomplishment

What about you? What is it that you want for yourself? How will your life be different when you're living your life more in line with your own values? How will you feel when you achieve your fitness and weight-loss goals? Who are you with? What are you doing? What season is it? What are you wearing? The more you can fill in the blanks, the clearer the vision and the closer you will be to living the life you deserve.

Getting to the truth of your "why" in your motivational mojo is the secret to success not only in your fitness goals but in all areas of your life.

There is no magic bullet (yet) to getting fit and losing weight. However, spending a few moments to think of what will internally motivate you to embrace positive change is worth its weight in gold.

Sometimes you just have to let go and give yourself permission to live your dream and be your best. But, why is this so hard to do?

Get Real: Facing What Is

As I shared with you in the last chapter, I completely get how our inner self-perception wreaks havoc on our sizzle. I have been there and done that. Let's dig deeper into the process and get busy with the tools on how to get *real*, get *radical*, and unleash your Inner Hottie self that is so ready to go.

Resistance to facing the music of our past is often what really causes diets to fail and exercise plans to get left by the wayside. Our commitment falls away when the negative self-talk rears its ugly head.

- Made to feel "less than" and ashamed when you were 5?

  Your body remembers.

- Called fat when you were 12?

  That memory is still lodged.

- Crushed in a love relationship?

  Yup, your body's got that stored as well.

News Flash: Our bodies store old memories like bulletproof vaults, whether we remember these

4. Are you ready to take immediate action to take your sexy fit self off the back burner of your life? If yes, why is *now* the time more than ever?

Excellent job. This work is not easy but is so important in attaining the freedom that the Inner Hottie Lifestyle Plan provides.

Now, let's move onto some fun stuff: celebrating your inner confidence and showing the world what you got going on.

Staying Positive in a Largely Negative World

Exude Confidence for the Sexy Glow

The key ingredient to success in life is this: "Attitude is everything." By focusing on the positive, we can do all the right exercises we need and eat all the right foods. Approaching life with stress and anger will never yield the results we desire.

Nothing opens the channels of healing and vitality more than an attitude of gratitude and positivity. If you want amazing results from your training program, bring amazing energy. How will you act, stand, breathe and move when you are living in a body with the spirit that you desire? What will you be doing, who will you be with and how will you feel when you are celebrating that ultimate success?

Exude confidence. Being confident draws people to you. A more *confident* you is a more *charismatic* you. Sometimes, in the beginning, you have to fake it 'til you make it, especially if you are trying something on for the first time.

You are a unique person with unique gifts and talents. The best thing to do is to be YOU, not some cheap imitation of you.

What we try to hide- our "perceived weaknesses" – are usually the place through which our greatness is born. And we fight like crazy to hide these parts of ourselves, especially when it's time to step into an amazing new version of ourselves.

Did I have what it took to build a multimillion-dollar business without taking a single business class? By all appearances, um, heck no! But you better believe I made a commitment to walk and talk like I did until I was living it, even with my teeth chattering and knees shaking.

I believe you can live with that level of courage too.

You are human. Don't be afraid of your humanness. People want to see the real you, not some phony imitation.

Celebrate Your Best YOU by Bringing Your Uniqueness to the World

It's not always easy to define what is most unique about ourselves. This is why I believe it is so important to work with a coach you trust to help you bring out the best version of you to the world. A coach or mentor will help you channel and define what makes you unique. The results will bring greater success in all aspects of your life, with way faster results.

Where I begin with my clients is helping them get clear on where their strengths lie. Often it can be even more subtle, like understanding our limiting beliefs that get in the way of our own way so we can show up more authentically.

So many of us understand that we shouldn't dim others' lights by living in judgment of who they are, but we usually don't give ourselves the same courtesy.

It is my belief that we are all here for a divine assignment, something that is totally and wonderfully unique. My question to you is: are you ready to uncover and fully embrace that part of you?

This is not definitely not the easiest process, however, it is a crucial step to bring the charismatic and confident YOU front and center in your own life.

Be kind to yourself in the process, and show grace to the imperfect and evolving you. There is no dress rehearsal. Live all out each and every day like this is your final rodeo. You can never get this beautiful moment back.

And remember, when you bump into people who have bad attitudes, please don't let it affect you. Understand often their grumpiness is their own issue and has nothing to do with you. Remain in your greatness. Be sure to share your hopes and dreams with those who will support you on your journey. And most importantly, enjoy the ride.

Celebrate your positivity.

Attitude is everything. Confidence is sexy.

Tidbit: Adopting daily micro-steps will lead to your most amazing kick-butt life. Achieving your fitness and health goals requires adding daily actions to your schedule. You can do this.[1][2]

 Hottie Hazard – Not Getting Enough Shut-Eye

Confession: This is the hardest hazard for me to avoid, and I am sure this is true for many of you. Life is so full and busy and, darn it, we don't want to miss a thing.

But the bottom line is this: Your Inner Hottie factor needs replenishing daily and that means putting your beautiful temple to rest. The latest studies show that the lean people out there sleep more than the less lean. Sleep-deprived peeps have less control over their food choices – that's a fact. I know that when I'm tired, the first thing I want is sugar, and lots of it.

Another factoid: Getting less sleep decreases our body's ability to regulate glucose levels, which increases insulin production, leading to weight gain and a boatload of other scary health issues.

So, sleep, rest, restore. You deserve it and your inner Inner Hottie self will thank you with more joy, increased energy and a stronger and fitter body to fuel you throughout the day.

Making your health and hotness a priority takes passion and commitment. Avoiding living-fit hazards will get you where you want to go quicker and with greater energy and vitality than you can imagine.

Keep moving. Stay in action. Eat clean and make your life amazing.

Chapter 5

Motivational Mojo: Tolerations – Giving a Boot to your Hot Mess

Are you ready to have massive freedom and to let your inner hottie shine all out? By zapping tolerations, you will gain freedom and fun. And that's the sizzling-hot truth.

Tolerations: little (or big) things that you have been tolerating in life that eat away little pieces of your confidence, pleasure, happiness, and joy.

By zapping tolerations, you will immediately experience the following:

- less stress
- increased productivity
- easier relationships
- healthier boundaries
- increased self-esteem and self-worth
- inner glow and greater flow

So, what is standing in your way of living a full-on juicy life? Be honest with yourself. What changes are you ready to make?

After reviewing some suggested tolerations, mark the ones that resonate with you most. Feel free to add your own. Then, start taking action to remove these tolerations one by one. Be consistent and attack these tolerations like a beast.

This exercise is a gamechanger for my clie[nt]
the same will apply to you. The freedo[m]
handle your tolerations is immense. I had o[ne]
after handling her tolerations, increased he[r]
40%. Another client lost 40 pounds when h[e]
his top three tolerations. You can achieve these
wonderful results too!

Here you go:

- Not enough storage space for all my office files.

- Not staying committed to my workout goals.

- A desk stacked to the sky.

- Peeling wallpaper or chipped paint.

- A love partner I am not truly connected with.

- Being overweight.

- Disorganized work systems.

- Poor grooming and self-care.

- Messes in certain areas of your home.

- Not enough time scheduled for chilling out.

- Not enough time spent alone.

- Not setting time aside to meditate and pray.

- Not saving money every month.

- Not getting paid enough for my work.

- Tolerating people who blow you off at the last minute.

Excessive clutter.

Dirty car.

- Investments that should be re-evaluated but haven't been.

- House in disrepair.

- Not having a spare key for the car.

- Long honey-do list.

- Not enough sex and intimacy.

- Spending no time on your own personal growth.

- Mortgage and car payments are out of my comfort zone.

- Negative attitudes of people at my work.

- Poor customer service and inadequate responses from vendors.

- Eating too much sugar and salt.

- Low levels of reserves.

- Too many possessions that need to be cleaned.

- Drinking too much.

- Unnecessary demands from spouse and children.

- Lack of creative outlets and hobbies.

- Not enough fun.

- Being part of a profession where I can no longer relate to the goals and standards.

- Knowing all my debt will not be paid off when I retire or have a baby.

- Inadequate retirement fund.

- Demands on my time by people in my life that stress me out.

- A former spouse who does not support co-parenting.

- Being misunderstood or not being listened to.

- Lack of deep friendships.

- Messy garage, basement, etc.

- Taxes not complete.

- Someone close to you with an unaddressed drug or alcohol problem.

- Unattractive underwear, old towels, spices, pantry items.

- Going to the doctor.

- Electronics and wires that you don't know what they go to.

- Not knowing where your money is going.

- Poor relationship with your parents or in-laws.

- Not getting enough physical touch.

- Unorganized tools.

- Dirty windows.

- Unresolved grief.

Clothes that don't fit or are out of style.

Burned out lightbulbs, poor lighting.

Excess stuff in your trunk.

- Socks with holes.

- Being ghosted again.

- Ugly shoes.

- A bad kisser.

- Under sink mess, dresser drawers, closet a mess

Write it down:

Write your top five tolerations down here. Please feel free to write down your own.

1.

2.

3.

4.

5.

Start crossing off tolerations from your list today. This exercise is going to change your life. Start zapping these stressors so you can start living your life with greater sizzle and increased energy to boot.

Celebrate and Radiate

News Flash: The process of moving into your greatness is wonderful, amazing, and a little scary too. Be prepared for all of it.

I realized that as I leveled-up my life and moved into my "BIG," the part that scared me the most was not knowing who I would be if I wasn't my self-loathing and self-doubting self. Who knew that the biggest fear I had was keeping my fittest and most fabulous self on the back burner of life?

And the result? Be prepared to have people drawn to you who normally wouldn't even have said hello before-dogs, people at the grocery store. This power of attraction thing just starts happening.

It's actually quite simple. When you are at peace, your concern for what others think of you no longer matters.

This is not about ego.

This is not about being phony.

This is about being fully you, the powerful you, the silly you, the vulnerable you.

This is you, just being you.

This is about living in your true and authentic self. When we celebrate ourselves, our uniqueness, our beauty in and out, the world shifts. And I promise you this: you'll find smiles, laughter, prosperity, abundance, kisses, parking spots, you name it!

Lastly, and perhaps more importantly, by celebrating your Inner Hottie self, you serve as a positive role model to others: your kids, friends, intimate partners. This is what authenticity and integrity look like, and I am telling you, you will be mighty pleased.

So go claim your sexy fit self. Carry your inner celebration with you wherever you go. With a sparkle in my eye and knowing that you are so completely and totally worth it, I celebrate you completely.

The opposite of courage is not fear but inaction. Stay in action. Success happens one micro-step at a time. You got this.

Chapter 6

Motivational Mojo: The Holistic Approach to Your Health and Hotness

As a media expert, high-performance coach, and athlete, I am no stranger to the public eye. As a result, I'm often approached by people who want to ask about my physique. They think that, hey, all I need to do is lose weight and my whole entire life will be rocking all the way around. Not necessarily....

That's like saying that people who win the lottery are happier than the rest of us because now they don't have money worries. Simply not true. If you disagree, explain the staggering number of winners who end up bankrupt after they burn through their entire bankroll?

Money doesn't buy happiness and neither does skinny.

The fact is that people who end up rocking their weight loss and fitness goals really do experience a full life transformation. It changes their entire way of perceiving themselves and their relationships.

It isn't just about the weight. It's a *lifestyle.*

What these successful life-changers have found is that their transformation occurred from the inside out. They were ready to release self-defeating patterns and behaviors that kept them in bodies that really did not reflect who they were on the inside.

Like I said, Inner Hottie is an inside job.

To experience a rock-star-quality transformation, we have to change how we experience our own realities.

So, how about you? What changes have you decided to take on to let go of and embrace the new you?

We know who we are, deep in our souls, if we really listen. When what's reflected on the outside doesn't match what's on the inside, we're filled with unrest and unease. We overeat, stress out, toss and turn at night, and bitch and complain because we know we are not living in our best and highest selves. We just know it.

The Inner Hottie Lifestyle Plan is about balancing our inner and outer mojos so we can live lives of integrity – body, mind, and soul. This is good stuff! You can do this.

You are worthy of having your body reflect the inner you – that strong, sexy, and vibrant spirit that lies within, waiting to be reborn. Today is the day to take on the challenge of living your greatest and best life yet. The world is ready to see YOU.

Hottie Hazard – Skipping Meals. Hey, I'm Just Not Hungry

Nothing makes us feel less hot than when we crash midday from lack of proper nutrition. Yuck.

You know what I am speaking of? That mid-day crash when you feel like you've fallen and you can't get back up. Maybe you reach for a Snickers and a latte because that's your cure-all to lift you up and keep you rolling..

The real deal? Starving yourself typically backfires. When you don't fuel your machine, your body goes into starvation mode and your metabolism slows to a trickle.

Then what happens next? You binge at night on calorie-laden food. And guess what? Your body stores those extra yum-yum calories as fat!

To attain and maintain a lean and sexy body, start with breakfast every day and fuel your body with a steady state of healthy foods with proper proportions of both calories and macros. (More on that later in Chapter 14.)

Note on intermittent fasting: I understand that there is a lot out there in social media land on intermittent fasting and many new diet regiments. However, what I have found with my clients is that the best way to begin is to start connecting with healthy food choices at regular intervals to reboot your metabolism and touch back into your physiological and psychological well-being. As with any nutrition plan, please be sure to check with your doctor and/or your health practitioner in regards to your specific health and wellness needs.

Chapter 7

Motivational Mojo: Why Living a Life of Integrity Is Sexy

Integrity: adherence to moral principles; honesty; wholeness.

To be our best, we must be whole. We are required to take personal responsibility for our actions *and* inactions, respond honestly and fully in our conversations, honor our bodies and respect our relationships and our environments.

When we are **in a state of integrity**, we experience:

- less conflict
- more self-acceptance
- greater inner-peace
- better overall health
- decreased anxiety

When we are **out of integrity**, we often experience:

- continual disturbances
- frustrations
- conflict in relationships
- self-sabotage
- distress
- even depression and acute loss of hope

Interesting to note: According to neuroscientists, we are only conscious of about **5 percent** of our cognitive activity, so most of our decisions, actions, emotions, and behavior depends on the 95 percent of brain activity that goes beyond our conscious awareness.

Yikes!

So then how the heck can we be in integrity when the majority of our thoughts are unconscious??

The answer? We must work super, super hard to counteract the negative talk by paying close attention to our thoughts, feelings, and relationships. This requires developing the personal development skills necessary to become more conscious of what was previously unconscious.

The most difficult part is when we get all excited about a great opportunity or a vision for our future, and our own unconscious minds/ego goes overboard to crush our excitement.

Crazy, right? Our own thoughts are the biggest dream-dashers

Not our parents, our boss, our spouse, our kids.
Actually, our own thoughts derail us.

What I have seen in my work as a coach is that so many people I met have gone only so far in life and then metaphorically pull into a parking lot along the way, and park.

Are you parked? Are your hopes and dreams stuck in a traffic jam that you created through your own limited thinking? Are you frozen in fear with your foot on the brake instead of the accelerator of your life?

Are you in a dead-end job? Do you accept an overweight and out-of-shape body as your norm? Are you existing in a passionless relationship? Feeling spiritually empty?

Isn't it time to put your car into gear and drive?

No one ever became great by imitation. Imitation is limitation.

Dare to be who you are.

What are you giving up to play it safe? Living a life outside of integrity keeps fear alive. Fear is just a condition that your mind creates to keep you parked.

If you have come this far, my bet is that you are ready to make the decision to no longer accept a smaller game.

There is only one life designed just for you. YOURS. Dare to live the best version of you.

Now, let's put our car in drive and hit the road and create a plan to live your best life with greater integrity and confidence.

Write it down:

1. What does the word integrity mean to you

2. How do you know when you are living in integrity?

3. When you are not living in integrity – how do you know?

4. What does your body tell you? How do you feel?

5. What does your mind tell you? What are the stories or dialogues that replay?

ain, knowledge is power. The more you know, the better you grow. Your path to greatness will not always be clear, but don't let your vision be clouded in fear and doubt. You are here for great things.

Stay in action. Eat clean, exercise, and keep pressing past fear by filling your thoughts with positive affirmation and a clear-cut action plan for success. Be crystal clear on what you ultimately want.

If you believe with this conviction, you will move mountains. Choose to be open to possibility. Choose to say yes!

Hottie Hazard – Jumping on the Latest Fad Diet Bandwagon

Sorry, but there is no magic pill or restricted food diet (lemon, water and cabbage soup anyone?) that will quickly melt away your extra weight and keep it off.

Lifestyle switch-up is the only sure-shot way to create long-lasting change. Stick to the basics of eating clean, smaller portions with greater frequency. This and getting that booty moving every day is the magic combo.

Chapter 8

Motivational Mojo: Getting Clear by Creating Healthy Relationships

As you move through your Inner Hottie transformation, you will experience some emotions that are best addressed outright:

1. Bewilderment
2. Intolerance of people lying and not being straight-shooters
3. Hurt feelings that seem out of context with the given situation unexplained emotional fogginess
4. Clarity of ideas
5. Moments of bliss that you just can't explain
6. Uncontrollable laughter
7. Uncontrollable tears
8. Deep feelings of unexplained peace
9. Joy and Bliss
10. Relief

You just start feeling different.

Really different.

And you can't quite put your finger on what it is.

People around you notice it too and are not really sure what has happened either. Where is the "old" you?

Congratulations. You are moving into a transformational period where your old ways of being no longer serve you, and your greater calling – the Bigger and Better YOU – is waiting to be born. Welcome.

This is the moment you have been waiting for. So why does it feel so... strange?

As your coach, I am here to help, support and challenge you through this crazy stage. You are going to be fine. More than fine – you are going to be amazing.

Let's go over some strategies you can use to make this easier for you and those who surround you. We will start with talking some more about these variable emotions through personal transformation.

First, keep in mind the following: some reactions or emotions may seem out of context. This may be especially true if a particular issue is laden with emotional wounds that have not been addressed, holding a whole history of hurts – you may unknowingly react out of context to the actual event at hand.

For example:

Your spouse is late, without calling, and shows up just after you have put dinner on the table. You flip out.

or:

Your business partner sent out a proposal that you had not yet reviewed and given your stamp of approval. You seethe.

Reactions? Normal. Why is that, you may ask?

What is happening is that old wounds are surfacing so you can resolve them once and for all. If tardiness or not getting a say in something that is important to you really truly matters, then you are being faced with a great opportunity to clear that up head-on. Use these opportunities to live in a new level of integrity and clarity.

Make sense?

This is called **creating healthy boundaries**. It is part of maintaining a higher level of self-care. This is about being clear on what is acceptable to you, without judgment of others, so you are more aligned with your authentic self.

Will there be bumps on the way? Sure.

Will you need to say you're sorry a few times? Perhaps.

Will others be clear on what is important to you and why? Absolutely.

Congratulations for putting your integrity of self at the center of your Inner Hottie transformation. It takes some work, but the steps you take here and now are not only invaluable, they are essential to your transformation.

Again, understand that transformation requires adapting to new ways of being and communicating and it stirs up some real juicy stuff. It surfaces now with such power and intensity because this is a reminder of what you must release to be finally free of your past. And this, my friend, is way good.

To be clear: When you are in the midst of it, it may not feel good. But soon the clarity and release you experience will be so worth it. I promise. I have worked with many people who have been challenged through this scenario. You will make it through, as well – more powerful and focused than ever.

As you move into a higher level of integrity, your goals become more attainable. Success occurs with less effort and more ease. You feel an overall greater sense of peace. You experience an increased sense of abundance. Your relationships are richer.

Important Self Care Tip: Talk issues out with your coach, therapist, or accountability partner. Write in a journal or meditate, but *do not give up on your Inner Hottie dream* and fail to face the work that your breakthrough life requires.

Quitters tend to be more concerned with how far they have to go versus how far they have come. That is not you. *You* are not a quitter.

Stay clear on your goals, choose action over reaction, and stay in self-love and self-acceptance. Picture how you want conversations to end up and hold steady on that vision. Be less worried about being right. Be most concerned with staying in your integrity and in grace.

Congratulations for digging in and committing to your highest and best vision of you.

Write it down:

Please review the eliciting questions bel
answers may surprise you. Be kind in your re
emotions can come up that have been latent fc

As you think about your transformation, ask the following:

1. What are some things that could get in the way of achieving your goals and living a breakthrough life?

2. Are there people you think may not support your personal Inner Hottie transformation?

3. Why?

4. Please list 3 people who you believe will support your Inner Hottie dream.

5. Ask yourself this: if you do not attain your goals and dreams, what do you lose? Are you willing to take that risk?

Chapter 9

Motivational Mojo: Action Plan for Claiming Your Inner Hottie

Living Your Unique Vision and Creating a Life of Your Dreams

We were all put on this beautiful planet, in this abundant world, for a REASON. Each of us is unique with a desire to be self-defined. So why do we spend so much time letting others define it for us?

The best part of unleashing your Inner Hottie is really understanding that this whole process is an inside job: to discover your life purpose, to live in abundance, to revel in self-love and acceptance, and to serve at your highest level in your greatest good.

You cannot live this way if you are letting someone else write the agenda.

You are in charge of writing your own script. What stories do you want to be telling someday from your rocking chair? Commit to making them amazing.

To unleash your Inner Hottie requires **DAILY ACTION STEPS** so you can hit your Hottie bulls-eye. Sure, crappy things happen. Tragedy strikes every life, but if you develop your resilience muscle and keep self-love and acceptance at your core, you will be amazed by how your life looks and feels.

I want it for you: a burning sizzle that keeps you roaring with passion and desire, which is possible because you use daily actions to live your best life.

Creating a vision statement is the necessary framework for creating a powerful and amazing life. It provides direction for

Ready to make a big change, but don't know where to start.

I hear it all the time.

This happens when we don't put a plan and structure for our dream in place. As a result, our commitment waivers. Cue the stinkin' thinkin' cycle, which begins anew, and bam, we find our head in the fridge looking to feed our disappointment and disgust...

Why do we keep doing this?

Well, unless you have a crystal clear vision of what you want, you will end up beating yourself to a pulp because all you experience is failure.

Kate's Behavior Modification Tip: Sometimes we have to return to Pavlov and create a physical action to replace our negative thinking. I go right to breathing. I breathe in peace and blow out anxiety. Trust me, you can regain PEACE in one breath! Pick an action that works for you, such as tapping on your thigh, rubbing between your eyes, pushing into your palm. Create an action that centers you. Make this a habit to restore your inner peace.

"So, Kate, what is a Vision Statement, anyway?"

Vision Statement: A guiding light that
darkness, illuminating your hopes and
vision statement is a written description of
to live your most amazing life. It serves as a
how you live every day.

Write it down:

To create a vision that motivates, encourages and drives you, consider the following:

1. What is the most positive and affirming mental image you can create of yourself in the not-too-far-off future?

2. Where are you?

3. What are you doing?

4. Who are you with?

5. What are you wearing?

6. How is the weather?

7. What emotions are you experiencing as you celebrate your new Inner Hottie life?

Ready, Set, GO!

OK, now it is time to put pen to paper and write down in detail your vision for your Claim Your Inner Hottie Lifestyle. This includes what you will be doing and how you will be meeting and greeting the best version of you. Be sure to write in present tense, as though you have already accomplished this vision.

- Write about things you enjoy doing on a daily basis.
- Write about what you value.

- Write about what fulfills you.

In my amazing Inner Hottie vision, I am

NICE WORK!

Please keep this description somewhere where you can revisit it at least weekly.

Inner Hottie Goal Implementation

"All our dreams can come true, if we have the courage to pursue them."

— *Walt Disney*

Now that you have created a vision statement, let's add some spark by putting your dream into action. Start by reviewing your vision statement and extracting two to three events that you can create some action steps around to bring your sexy sizzle to center stage.

Remember: A Goal Is Just a Dream with a Timeline

A goal needs to be realistic and measurable. Now, when I say realistic, I mean that if your goal is to lose weight, don't create some unrealistic goal such as losing 10 pounds for the weekend or running a marathon at the end of the month when you haven't walked around the block in the past month.

I hate to burst your bubble, but a healthy and realistic weight loss goal is roughly 1 to 2 lbs. a week. Planning for more than that will unfortunately be setting yourself up for failure and disappointment. Please don't do that. I want you to succeed, so let's be sure to set up goals that you can nail.

Putting a timeline on your goals is another crucial element to your transformation. Working within a timeline will require you to stay in action on a daily basis. Action breeds success. Your daily habits create your reality. If you are ready to up-level, make the commitment to set a deadline for the date of accomplishment. You deserve it.

Let's create a timeline for your goal, starting with a month as a framework.

Sample goals: lose fat, gain muscle, develop six-pack abs, workout every day for a certain length of time. Eliminate or add something to your diet, drink 64 oz. of water daily. What's yours? Be specific.

GOAL: ⟹ _____

RESULT:_____

Week 1

Action: I commit to

Week 2

Action: I commit to

Week 3

Action: I commit to

Week 4

Action: I commit to

At the end of one month I will

Start with the end in mind, making the goal challenging as well as exciting..

Great work! Now share your goal with an accountability partner or coach.

Hottie Hazard – Oops! Missed My Workout! Oh, well!

Your Inner Hottie News Flash: Moving that body of yours is NON-NEGOTIABLE, if you really want it to manifest the body you desire. You said you wanted it, didn't you? I could have sworn I heard you say that you wanted it BAD…

Staying committed to your Inner Hottie vision is not going to be easy, but it will be worth it. Anyway, I have never heard of anyone saying, "Shoot, I regret working out today." Not ever.

Keep leaning in. Success requires taking forward steps every day to win. You got this!

Chapter 10

Motivational Mojo: Fear & Resistance –Being Your Own Stick in the Mud

Set Yourself Free Using the Power of Affirmation

Studies show it takes 21 to 28 days to establish a new habit, so expect resistance and challenges at the beginning of implementing the Inner Hottie Lifestyle Plan.

The bigger and bolder your new vision is, the greater the likelihood that you will experience internal resistance and fear. Your unconscious mind does not always play fair.

This is when having previously completed your **vision statement** *in Chapter 9* comes into play in a big way. Please keep at it and stay on track.

You will soon reach the wonderful place, the tipping point, where you begin to experience the positive benefits of lifestyle change that far outweigh your old and outdated habits that have kept you out of the red-hot zone.

Stay committed even when you want to quit. The feelings of being overwhelmed will pass. You are worthy of a breakthrough life.

When you're thinking of releasing old habits and adopting new ones, picture a rubber band. The further you pull, the greater the resistance. It's time for you to pick up a bigger band.

Harness the Power of Resistance

It's important that we understand that resistance is just part of the Inner Hottie game. Notice when it comes up, address it and keep moving forward.

Here I will highlight ways that resistance can show up in our lives during our transformation.

☺ Days 1 and 2 – WE make the commitment to be our best self and take bold action. Woo hoo, you feel excited! Unstoppable! "I can do this!"

:-/ 3rd day – not as easy, enthusiasm wanes. "Hmm, well, ok I will go to the gym, but I don't really feel like it… Chicken and broccoli again…"

☹ 2nd week – generally the hardest time period. Enthusiasm has left the building. "This sucks." "I don't feel like it." "No one else is doing this stuff." Keep at building new habits and hold the vision. Keep eating clean. Keep moving! You can do it! Don't quit!

:-/- ☺ 3rd and 4th weeks – a little easier; you start seeing results! "Wow, I feel more energetic." "Hey, my face looks thinner." "What happened to my sugar craving? It's gone!" Congrats! Celebrate every win!

Remember this important acronym:

FEAR – False Expectations Appearing Real!

You are a failure only if you fail to get up or blame someone else for pushing you down. You are bigger than your fear.

Believe in your possibility!

Tapping into Power of Affirmation: Be Confident in Your Success

Affirmation: a statement or proposition that is declared to be true.

I am shocked at some of the things I hear people using as "affirmations" for themselves to get motivated, such as: "I don't want to look like a fat pig anymore", "I'm sick of feeling like crap", and "I make myself sick." These are real life examples of what people tell me when I ask them what motivates them to make a positive lifestyle change. Ouch.

Using positive affirmations takes practice. However, if you keep using more affirmative language to state your wishes and intentions, you will discover that dreams really do come true.

Practice saying the affirmations below out loud and see which ones resonate with you or write down some of your own.

Try these on for size:

- I am worthy of a healthy and fit body.
- I am ready to embrace the Inner Hottie lifestyle.
- I deserve all the good that shows up in my life.
- I see myself moving with ease and grace.
- I am ready to live my life full out.

- I am here to do great things.
- My body is a temple worthy of extreme self-care.
- I deserve to feel sexy and strong.
- I am powerful beyond measure.
- I am a bright light in the world.
- I celebrate all that is good about me.
- I forgive myself for any wrongs I have done, perceived or imagined.
- I live in complete integrity in all aspects of my life.
- I represent peace, love, and joy in the world.

Write it down:

Your top three, feel free to add your own:

1.

2.

3.

Kate's Tip: I stick Post-it notes all over my house with affirmations when I am having a tough week. Visual reminders are great cues to keep us aligned with our vision by reminding us why we are worthy of achieving all that we desire.

Steps you can apply today to activate your inner mojo:

1. Start where you are, taking one micro-step at a time.
2. Keep practicing saying YES to your possibility. As soon as you hear your negative self-talk, hit the PAUSE button on your gremlins and push PLAY to your possibility. Sometimes tapping on one leg

to pause and on the other thigh to play helps reprogram your thinking and keeps you in the right lane to your big dream.

3. Lighten up! Laugh at yourself! Nothing shifts your experience more than laughter and joy.
4. Watch a funny movie/show.
5. Hang with people who lighten your spirit. Be that person for others.
6. Involve yourself in a community/church that lifts you up.
7. Practice random acts of service.

The most rewarding thing you can do if you feel stagnant about your lot in life is to open a service station. Nothing lifts us up more than when we serve others.

Great work.

Now it is time for the Clean Eats section of the Inner Hottie Lifestyle Plan.

Let's go

Part 3
The Claim Your Inner Hottie
Clean Eats Plan

Chapter 11

The Inner Hottie Clean Eats Mojo Revealed

What if I told you that with the Inner Hottie Lifestyle, you may potentially eat more than you are used to? You will no longer suffer from the 3 p.m. afternoon slump. You will experience increased vitality and energy?

It's true! And I can't wait to share the how-to's with you.

But first, a tad more on my backstory…

I can recall how 20 years ago, after I gave birth to my third child, my desire to finally get back into shape and leave self-flagellation behind reached critical mass. I was ready to get my body back. So, I hired a trainer named Brian. He wanted me to keep a food log as part of our work together. The first time I turned it in, he said "You are not eating enough."

What? How could that be? I thought I was doing so well. Cripes, I even doctored the log to try and impress him.

Wrong.

"Wait! I thought I had done so well over the last few days of food tracking!" I exclaimed.

Nope, he told me, shaking his head disappointedly. "Not enough and not the right kinds of foods."

Not enough? Not the right foods? Humpf. I was insulted.

Okay, so maybe he had a point there. I looked at my bloated and swollen body in the mirror that night. Apparently, what I had been doing was not working. I realized then and there that if I wanted my sexy back, it was high time for me to get re-educated to the how-to's of eating clean.

CLEAN EATS is eating foods that fuel YOUR BEAUTIFUL, AMAZING machine. CLEAN EATS get your motor running optimally for maximum energy and fat-burning capabilities. CLEAN EATS allow you to live the Inner Hottie Lifestyle.

Sounds good? Great, then let's dig in...

Chapter 12

Clean Eats and Emotional Eating – Reboot Your Stinkin' Thinkin'

EATING CLEAN: fueling your machine with self-love and healthy eats to maximize your mojo

Before we dig into nutrition the Inner Hottie way, I would like to address the super important issue of how so many of us use food to soothe, not to fuel, our bodies and souls.

The ultimate love for ourselves begins with what passes through our lips on a daily basis. Extreme self-care requires us to take a good, hard look at our emotional connection with food.

It's not only *what* we eat. It's *why* we are eating that holds the real key to transforming our bodies and our lives.

TRUTH: We don't eat just for fuel. Often we eat to soothe hurt feelings or stuff pains and wounds that make us feel yucky.

Sure, I'm fit, but that doesn't mean I haven't gone through the same struggles my clients and listeners have gone through. I get it. Really, I do. I can remember the self-loathing and the food battles like they were yesterday.

And that is the truth. I have made different *choices* for myself.

So can you.

I found that a huge part of why preparing for a Bikini Fitness Competition is so challenging is exactly this: I had to face my patterns of how I used food (as a reward and to cope). And I am telling you, the process to self-awareness wasn't always pretty!

No longer using food as a "source to soothe", I am forced to deal head-on with any unresolved issues in my life, and the process can be painful. Okay, not "can be" – it IS.

But just like when a monk goes into silent retreat or an athlete prepares for a big competition, they understand that the journey starts and ends *within*. This doesn't change for you and me as we embrace living a more healthy and fit lifestyle.

It would be so much easier if we could just say, "Hey, I'm going to lose 10 pounds," and we did it. But the truth is we shed way more than the physical weight when we embrace a lifestyle transformation. Old patterns and behaviors, like old luggage we haul behind us, have to be kicked to the curb.

Through any transformation, personal issues surface (past feelings of rejection, fear, loneliness, etc.). This part of your Inner Hottie rebirth is not always easy, but so worth it.

So, why do many of us experience epic failures in our health goals? One word: FEAR. Fear of failure. Fear of success. Fear of letting go. Fear of judgment. Fear of the unknown. Fear of… you name it. Our fear and resistance to face the music of our pasts are often the real causes of diet failures and abandoned exercise plans.

Letting Go: Kissing Goodbye to What No Longer Serves You

When we move fully into our transformation to embrace our Inner Hottie, the relationships around us and within us suddenly look like they need some serious polishing.

What are you tolerating in your life that has to go – person, place, thing, behavior? We must name it so we can deal with it in a healthy manner. It is time to reframe your life by releasing self-sabotaging language, thoughts, and behaviors so we can finally be free to BE.

And the benefits of having tolerations resolved? Delicious and yummy freedom from self-sabotage, self-loathing, and any other self-defeating ways of being.

Please review the previous chapter 5 on Tolerations and be sure some of your tolerations include releasing patterns or behaviors around emotional eating. If there aren't any, go ahead and add them to the list. You are going to love crossing these off in the not-too-distant future for sure. Be ready for some giddy excitement when that day comes. And it will.

Free Tolerations Worksheet

and some time considering the following

1. What does food mean to me? (Please fill in the space with as many adjectives or nouns as you can come up with.)

   Food is…

2. What changes in my diet am I ready to embrace to release the weight that no longer serves me?

3. What self-sabotaging behavior are you ready to let go of?

4. Please write below any new eating habits and behavior changes you now embrace that will allow you to unleash your fit self wholly. You got this.

I will start today to:

Now please complete the following:

My Inner Hottie Freedom to Be My Best Self Mainifesto

Today I, _____, am ready
to   release

_____

_____

_____.

I know that this behavior no longer serves me. I will take
the following action, _____

_____

_____

_____

_____

_____, so that I can
release my inner hottie and attain the body I desire, the
lifestyle that reflects who I am, and the peace that I
deserve – because I am worthy!
Lovingly signed by:

_____

I encourage you to keep your Inner Hottie Manifesto someplace handy so you can read it aloud three times in a row, two times a day, preferably when you wake up and when you go to bed each day.

Bravo for taking this bold step. You are amazing.

Kate's Love Note to you beautiful peeps who struggle with food binging, anorexia, or any other ways to quell our sorrow, anger, loneliness, or dead-on grief: You are not alone. You deserve more. You are worthy of self-love and self-acceptance.

If this is you, please reach out to a coach or therapist who can help you face your emotions so you can be free to soar. The world awaits your brilliance.

Now let's dig into the Inner Hottie nutritional nuggets, shall we?

Chapter 13

The Claim Your Inner Hottie Clean Eats Lifestyle

Nutritional Mojo

"Can't I just do the treadmill and be done?"

So many of us are under the illusion that in order to look sizzling-hot like the latest hit Influencer on TikTok, we just have to get on the treadmill and cut out a couple of fast-food runs.

Well, I am here to burst that bubble, and quick.

From my experience, your nutrition, not exercise, is 70% of the Inner Hottie game.

"Eeek," I hear you scream! "This cannot be! I was just born fat, my whole family is overweight, my husband makes me eat it, my metabolism is just slow. My extra weight has nothing to do with my nutrition." Blah, blah, blah...I have heard it all, trust and believe.

Clean eating is the pathway to your fitness paradise. In order to live the Inner Hottie Lifestyle, you have to be all in on cleaning up your nutrition so you can gain the quickest benefits and regain the vitality and sizzle you long for.

"But wait, Kate, what about the other 30%?"

Great question.

From my experience, the other 30% can be divided into the following:

20% exercise

10% genetics

Now, let's dig into *why* nutrition plays such a crucial role. Then we will talk about how we can use exercise to put your sexy machine into overdrive.

Believe it or not, the odds of nature are *stacked in your favor* – and not vice versa. This is worth repeating: The odds of nature are actually stacked in your favor, *if* you are ready to make adjustments to what, when, and how you eat.

For some of you, this may be a small shift. For others, this may be a much bigger change-up. I get this. But what is more important is how big the desire is to manifest your best self, who is just waiting to be unleashed. You have the power and strength to claim this powerful person from within using the right action plan, designed by *you*!

By applying the **Clean Eats Action Plan** and embracing the exercises in this book, you can peg the red on your hotness odometer. I look forward to hearing about your amazing success. Please email me with any questions here: kate@kate-mckay.com

To review, in order to live the Inner Hottie Lifestyle, you must adopt the Eat Clean and Get Fit Game Plan, which includes:

- Eating all kinds of yummy foods that convert your body from a fat-manufacturing machine to a fat-burning machine.
- Incorporating strength training into your regimen to increase your muscle mass for increased fat-burning power.
- A moderate cardiovascular exercise program that will round out your full body renovation.

If weight loss is your goal, jump in and feel confident that you will lose the weight at a rate of 1 to 2 pounds per week as a result of adopting the **Eat Clean and Get Fit Lifestyle.**

Think about it: In 28 days you could be 5 to 10 pounds lighter, increase your fat-burning muscle significantly and experience greater energy and sex appeal!

How amazing will that be?

Celebrate each and every success you experience. Don't wait for someone else to celebrate for you. Let the celebration come from within.

I am the first one to admit that I love food. I love how food – the preparing and sharing of it – is one of the most beautiful opportunities for experiencing community with the people we love and care for.

One of my greatest pleasures in life is making awesome meals for my kids and friends. Food is nurturing. It shows caring, generosity and love.

The sad reality is that two out of three Americans are overweight or obese, and the problem is only getting worse. We have gone from viewing food as celebration to using it as a way to soothe and satiate all kinds of emotional and biological impulses.

It's clear the "quick fix, get skinny" diet culture we live right now is *not* working. We need to shift our fundamental ways of thinking, believing, and behaving to create a culture that is healthy and fit *from the inside out.*

The 90/10 Rule of the Inner Hottie Lifestyle Plan

I would like to introduce to you the 90/10 rule of the Inner Hottie Lifestyle Plan. Each day focus on getting at least 90% of your food choices from the Clean Eats Macronutrients listed in the following Chapter 14. The remaining 10% can be choices made from your cheat food favorites.

Now unfortunately that does *not* mean 10 Oreos, an extra grande super latte with extra cream and sugar, a fried platter with all the fixings. Because the key to weight management is this: portions matter.

You can still enjoy the flavors and foods you love and crave. But please accept that portions must be smaller. They will be just a sampling of what was once a much larger portion before.

For example, say your calorie allotment for the day is 1,800 calories. Your 90/10 breakdown looks like 1,500 calories for your Clean Eats around 200-300 calories for a yummy treat.

Take back your ability to savor your food. It is your right to find enjoyment in what you eat. I promise you, as you clean up your food choices, your craving for unhealthy food will fade.

When you adopt the Inner Hottie 90/10 rule, you'll not only be happier with how you look, you will also feel hotter than you've ever felt.

If you slip up, relax. One bad meal choice is no reason to send you into a tailspin of despair and self-loathing. You have the ability to *course-correct* one meal at a time, so embrace self-love and self-forgiveness. And watch in awe to see how your relationship with food once again becomes an experience of celebration.

Remember: You have the ability and the power to course-correct after a "cheat meal" or a binge that did not fuel or soothe your soul.

What's done is done. Jump on the clean eating track at the next meal. One binge does not define you. You are here to live in your magnificence. Focus on the amazing vision you have created for yourself and move forward confidently.

Hottie Hazard – Fat Burners and Cleanses

I am frequently asked my opinion on the latest fat-burning cleanse or other newfangled diet regimen. My answer is always the same:

There is no better Rx than eating clean, exercising your body, hydrating, and living in peace, self-love and self-acceptance. The Inner Hottie lifestyle is a way of life that no pill or diet can replace. Embracing the Inner Hottie Lifestyle Plan is about letting go of the fear and need for the quick fix, and realizing that you already possess everything you need.

Chapter 14

The Claim Your Inner Hottie Clean Eats System

Choosing Foods That Fuel the Machine

Now it's time to create a sound nutritional plan that will allow you to shed extra weight and live a life with more energy and vitality.

Let's start with some basic nutrition information on what healthy foods you will eat on the Inner Hottie Clean Eats Lifestyle Plan.

We will begin by reviewing the big three yummos – **macronutrients.**

MACRONUTRIENTS: proteins, carbs and healthy fats – all the goodness that supplies our bodies what they need for energy and repair.

1. **PROTEIN** – Consuming a healthy dose of protein is essential in the Inner Hottie Clean Eats Plan. Protein builds muscle, stabilizes blood sugars, feeds muscle tissues, and revs up your metabolism.

Excellent protein sources include the following:

lean beef cuts
chicken breast
turkey breast
ground turkey
eggs/egg whites

haddock

cod

halibut

flounder

salmon*

swordfish*

tuna*

protein powder (whey or vegan)

*These foods also are excellent fat sources that can count toward your daily fat needs.

By increasing your protein intake, you will most likely experience a decrease in hunger between meals, increased stamina, decreased fatigue, and a noticeably leaner physique.

When I first increased my protein consumption when I made the shift in my diet years ago, the change in my physique was dramatic. My body fat dropped by several percentage points, and I felt stronger and more energetic throughout the day. I was amazed.

2. **CARBOHYDRATES** – two ways – choose wisely.

Eek! The dreaded carb!

There is so much carb-bashing in the media. They've declared it as the main culprit in our country's obesity epidemic. For years, our "war on carbs" has saturated the market, instilling fear in millions and misinforming the multitudes.

So are carbs really that bad?

Well, yes and no.

As a society, our consumption of so much processed food has turned many of us into *carb junkies*. It is this processed crap that wreaks havoc on our metabolism and jacks our insulin levels up into the danger zone. Too many calories and an overconsumption of low quality food has been the *fuel of* our exploding obesity epidemic. We could all benefit from reducing our consumption of crapola.

The best way to conceptualize carbohydrates is to distinguish between the two classes. Then we can focus on how we will consume the "good ones" on the Inner Hottie Clean Eats Plan.

"But wait! How can we tell between a good carb and a bad carb?"

Great question.

The difference lies between low glycemic carbs and high glycemic carbs. The body assimilates and breaks these down differently.

High glycemic carbs or simple carbs are converted to sugar pronto. This increases insulin production and extinguishes your fat-burning capacity in a flash. These are not-so-great and need to be consumed at a minimum on the plan.

Examples of these dirty rotten culprits: *anything* with refined flour or sugar. Yup, all the white stuff filled with naughty sugars partnered with nasty fats that taste so good, but are like weapons of mass destruction to your hotness.

You know what I am talking about. All those "foods" that tempt our hotness factor and drop our fat-burning capabilities to zero. If you cannot resist these stinkers, I would suggest not keeping them in your house at all costs. Few people I know have the ability to not consume their favorite binge if it's anywhere in their vicinity, me included. I swear, these binge foods know when your emotions are weak and your "hunger" is high.

They are the trickiest, sneakiest devils, especially at the beginning of your Inner Hottie journey. Do not be tempted by their sugar sprinkle, sparkle, or tantalizing sales pitch. Slam the door, give them the back of your hand, and deny them at all costs.

It's hard. But it's possible. I believe in you.

Moving on to the *low glycemic foods*- **the good carbs**.

1. Good Carbs #1 – the stick-to-your-ribbers.
2. Good Carbs #2 – fresh and crunchy nibbles.

The Good Carbs #1

Here's your Inner Hottie Good Carbs #1 list:

oatmeal
brown rice
sweet potatoes
yams
rice cakes
Ezekiel bread (sprouted wheat)
whole grain pasta
spaghetti squash
pumpkin
quinoa

The Good Carbs #2

When we are talking Good Carbs #2, picture the rainbow, baby. Your shopping cart should be bursting with color.

Munch and crunch on your veggies. Why are these so good for you? Because you can munch on these items to your heart's content. Good Carbs #2 are filling, loaded with vitamins and minerals, and low in calories. They also slow down the absorption of your food, which boosts the fat-burning furnace.

Think of fiber rich foods as "nature's Brillo pad," giving your insides a good scrubbing. A clean system is a happy system. The high fiber content in these foods act like a magnet as it travels through your body. It binds with junk and pulls it out and through.

How cool is that?

Eating clean allows your body to absorb more good and slough off the bad so you can shine from the inside out.

Your good carb veggie list:

lettuce, all kinds, the darker the better
broccoli
zucchini
cauliflower
spinach
green beans
asparagus
peppers (red & green, yellow)

kale
onions
mushrooms

Fresh veggies are best.

HARSH TRUTH: Fruits are considered treats in the Inner Hottie Lifestyle. Sure, fruits have fiber; however, they are loaded with sugars that can skyrocket your insulin levels. Limiting fruit servings to one to two per day (¼ c berries, one small apple, etc. see below) keeps you in the red-hot sexy zone.

Your fruits list:

grapefruit – ½
berries (blue, rasp, straw, black) – ¼ cup small berries, ½ cup bigger berries
apple – 1 small
pear – 1 small
banana – ½

Taste Buds Reboot: Like any new habit, it can take two to three weeks for your taste buds and cravings to reset.

3. **FATS** – yes, fats! Hip, hip, hooray!

Like carbs, there are some good fats and some not-so-good fats. In the Inner Hottie Lifestyle Plan, it's important to differentiate between the two.

First, fat is essential for:

a. Energy. Gram for gram, fat is the best energy source. Fat provides 9 calories per gram. Carbs and proteins only provide 4 per gram.

b. Building healthy cell membranes for each and every part of your body including your brain. Without a healthy dose of good fat, your brain suffers and produces brain fog.
c. The absorption of important fat-soluble vitamins including A, D, E and K.
d. Making hormones – and we need those suckers. They make up some of the most important substances in the body, including prostaglandins and other hormonelike substances that regulate many of the body's functions.
e. Our skin, hair, and nails. We need fat to produce and keep our "lovelies" lovely.

The fats listed below contain essential fatty acids (EFA's). Our bodies don't produce our own supply, yet they play an important role in so many of our bodily functions, including healthy skin and happy muscles and joints.

Healthy fats:

almond oil
olive oil
flaxseed oil
fish/tuna oil
nuts (almonds, cashews, walnuts)
salmon
avocados
coconut oil
walnut oil

And the bad fats? Say adios to animal fats and other heavily processed foods that are jacked up with trans-fatty acids – these wreak havoc on your Inner Hottie Lifestyle Plan.

Those yuckos include all the white sugar, white flour, fat-laden convenience foods, bakery goods and fast-food junk that destroy your Hottie factor. A little taste is okay once in a while, but it is time to say farewell and au revoir to eating junk that only loads up your trunk.

Micronutrients

Vitamins and minerals serve an important role in regulating cell function, converting food into energy, and maintaining all biological functions. Personally, I am not a big proponent of popping pills. But, based on the fact that much of the produce we consume comes from heavily depleted soil, I believe it is a good idea to add a multivitamin-and-mineral supplement to your daily regimen. I also take a calcium supplement and vitamin D for strong and healthy bones.

Kate's Nutritional Tip: I am a minimal supplements kind o' girl. However, because it's tough to eat perfectly, I supplement my diet with a healthy vitamin and mineral supplement with no fillers or sugars. If you find one with vitamin D, it's a great bonus for strong and healthy bones.

Inner Hottie CLEAN EATS

SHOPPING LIST

PROTEIN	NON-STARCHY VEGETABLES	STARCHY VEGETABLES	FRUIT	GOOD FAT

Lean beef cuts	Lettuce	Oatmeal	Grapefruit	Almond oil
Chicken breast	Broccoli	Brown rice	Blueberries	Olive oil
Turkey breast	Zucchini	Sweet potatoes	Strawberries	Flaxseed oil
Ground turkey	Cauliflower	Yams	Raspberries	Fish/tuna oil
Eggs/egg whites	Spinach	Rice cakes	Blackberries	Almonds
Haddock	Green beans	Ezekiel bread	Apples	Cashews
Cod	Asparagus	Whole grain pasta	Pears	Walnuts
Halibut	Peppers	Spaghetti squash	Bananas	Salmon
Flounder	Kale	Pumpkin		Avocados
Salmon	Onions	Quinoa		Coconut oil
Swordfish	Mushrooms			Walnut oil
Tuna				
Protein powder				

https://courses.kate-mckay.com/clean-eats-playbook

Chapter 15

The Importance of Metabolism and Hydration

Eight Surefire Ways to Speed Up Your Metabolism

What does metabolism mean anyway? **Metabolism** is the process by which food is broken down and converted into energy. Who knew fueling your machine began at the cellular level.

Very few people genetically have a *"slow metabolism"* and, in fact, excessive dieting can sabotage your metabolic rate. Despite this fact, you can speed it up your metabolism by adding the following healthy habits into practice today:

1. Increase your muscle mass. People with higher levels of muscle tend to have a higher resting metabolic rate. That means you burn more calories just chilling out then less muscular folks do. Why? Muscle burns more calories than fat. According to the American Council on Exercise, each pound of fat burns only 2 calories a day, while muscle burns between 35 and 50 calories per day. That is a significant difference. Building calorie-consuming muscle will increase your metabolism.

2. Focus on intensity in your cardio program. Doing sustained-level intensity is great, but performing a higher level of cardio (or HIIT training) will be more

effective at increasing your metabolic rate. Examples of HIIT are a Spin class, a varied program on a treadmill or elliptical machine, or a jog workout of varying intensity for a minimum of 20 minutes to get your heart pumping and metabolism burning.

3. Embrace grazing. I know so many of our mothers told us to get out of the kitchen, stop snacking, to wait for dinner to eat; however, studies show that eating more frequently each day keeps the metabolism elevated. As a result, you will burn more calories throughout the day, even at rest. Stick to healthy lean proteins and vegetables as primary meal sources while focusing on fruit and healthy fats in snacks to keep you going in between.

4. Eat more protein. This tip has made the most significant difference to my personal physique. First, protein makes you feel full longer due to its density, reducing your need to binge on carbs to reach the same level of satiation. In addition, your body burns more calories to break down proteins (8 calories per gram for proteins vs. 4 for carbs). My clients hear this from me the most, "How is your protein level?" If you want a lean physique, your lean protein consumption must increase. Chicken, turkey, fish, and the occasional beef and pork are your best sources for increasing your metabolism and providing longer-lasting satiation.

Vegans take note: You will have a greater challenge in balancing your protein to carb ratio, but it is possible with careful planning and proper education. Please seek professional support here.

5. Eat your fiber. Higher-fiber foods (oatmeal, flaxseed, brown rice, sweet potatoes, asparagus, broccoli, green beans) provide steady, long-lasting energy and make you feel full and satisfied longer.

6. Drink up black coffee and green tea. A moderate amount of caffeine (1 to 2 cups a day) raises your metabolism slightly, increases concentration and improves heart health. Green tea also contains antioxidants that boost the immune system. Sip away, but limit caffeine to before 2pm to prevent negative implications to your sleep cycle.

7. Eat your healthy fats. Monounsaturated fats like olive oil help reduce cholesterol, triglycerides, and blood pressure. Polyunsaturated fats such as walnuts, almonds, flaxseeds, and salmon, are filled with omega-3s and reduce triglycerides and inflammation in the body. Coconut oil is all over yummo. Plus it has also shown to kill off sugar cravings.

8. Stay hydrated. When the body does not have enough water, several functions slow down, including the ability to burn calories. Muscles are roughly 65% to 70% water, so if they are not fully hydrated, they cannot perform as effectively, thus decreasing your calorie burn. Also, the body is not as efficient at burning fat when it is not hydrated for down shifting your metabolism.

How much water is still open to debate, but one study found that adults who drink 8 or more glasses of water a day burned more calories than those who drank 4 or fewer glasses a day. Shoot for 50% of your body weight in ounces as your base target amount.

Your metabolism is not a life sentence. By applying the principles above, you can boost the process to be the best version of you.

The Importance of Hydration

Did you know that water makes up 60% to 70% of your body? Crazy, right? Recent studies show that staying hydrated plays an important role in boosting your metabolism, which fuels your calorie-burning machine.

Proper hydration does the following:

- increases heart rate
- boosts metabolism
- increases the efficiency of your energy systems
- decreases and helps regulate appetite
- dilutes sodium retention which prevents bloating
- promotes healthy skin, your biggest organ
- increases blood volume so more oxygen gets into muscles

Water helps deliver nutrients to our organs and tissues, and helps in the removal of toxins and waste from the body. It also helps regulate body temperature.

Dehydration causes the following:

- increased wrinkles
- bags under the eyes
- headaches

- chapped lips
- constipation
- lethargy
- mood swings
- exhaustion

Doesn't reading this make you thirsty? I'm thirsty just writing about it. Go ahead and take a break in your reading and drink a quick 8ozs. Your body will thank you.

More on Clean Eats ahead. Don't miss it!

To sign up for Kate's free newsletter for more fitness and wellness tips, go to

https://courses.kate-mckay.com/cyib-workbook

Chapter 16

The Claim Your Inner Hottie Clean Eats Playbook

OK, so now it's time to move on to the nuts and bolts of the Inner Hottie Clean Eats Plan, including how much and how often.

Nutritional Tidbits

"How do I know how much to eat to attain my Inner Hottie goals?"

People have different goals based on their starting point and overall health, so it's important that you visit a doctor, a reputable nutritionist, or a trainer who has a high level of nutritional knowledge to set a calorie range that will most benefit your goals.

A simple rule of thumb: your daily calorie requirement is roughly 10 calories per pound of body weight. If you are looking to lose weight, base that amount on your ideal realistic target weight. If you are an athlete, the calorie requirement will be higher. Again, please speak to your doctor or nutritionist to ensure what would be your daily calorie target based on your goals.

Some important facts on macronutrients, and rough targets to shoot for:

Protein:

½ gram to 1 gram of protein per 1 lb. of lean body weight per day
4 calories per gram

Protein size that fits in your palm, 3 to 4 oz. per serving
Carbs:
½ to 1½ grams of carbs per 1 lb. of body weight
4 calories per gram

Fist size is a serving. Green veggies are the best bang for your buck.

Fats:

2-3 Tablespoons of fat a day.
9 calories per gram

Suggestions: Add 1 tablespoon of oil to your salad or veggies and you've got your fat calories covered. A tablespoon of walnuts in your oatmeal- delish.

Let's chat about portion control, the biggest Inner Hottie saboteur. Please refer to the chart below. When we truly see a visual cue on how much we should be eating, compared with what we currently consume, this can come as a terrible shock.

Hand Measurement	Foods	Calories (approx.)
Fist – 1 cup	Brown rice, sweet potato Fruit Veggies	200 150 40
Palm – 3 oz.	Meat Fish Poultry	160 160 160
Handful – 1 oz.	Nuts Raisins	170 85
2 Handfuls – 1 oz.	Chips Popcorn Pretzels	150 120 100

Thumb-size – 1 oz.	Peanut butter	170
	Hard cheese	100
Thumbnail-size – 1 tsp.	Cooking oil	40
	Mayonnaise, butter	35
	Sugar	15

Kate's tricks to adjust to eating smaller and healthier portions:

1. Drink a big glass of water before you eat. I drink room temperature water because I can drink it more easily.
2. Use a small salad plate or soup bowl to eat your meals.
3. Use juice glasses (6 to 8 oz.) to drink anything besides water.
4. Say goodbye to mindless eating. Concentrate on what you are eating and savor the flavors of your healthy foods. Turn off the tube and the screen.
5. Use baby spoons to eat dessert. It really makes you savor every bite.
6. Make a big batch of protein and veggie soup at least once a week.
7. Get adequate rest. A well-rested body tames binging.
8. Keep the junk out of the house if you know you cannot resist. Why put yourself through the torture?
9. Eat 3 oz. of protein before you go out to socialize to prevent overeating.

MEAL PLANNING FREQUENCY ON THE INNER HOTTIE LIFESTYLE PLAN:

Are you ready? This is it, Baby! The ticket to having the body of your dreams...

- Eat!
- Eat More of the Good Stuff!
- Eat Less of the Bad Stuff!
- Eat Clean at Least 90% of the Time!
- Eat More Often!

Yes! 4-5 times a day, every 3-4 hours a day, is a must to get the body of your dreams and the energy and vitality you need to live an amazing life. The most important thing to realize is that this is not a huge calorie gut, but smaller meals/snacks at greater frequency.

Here's how the math works for a 5 day meals frequency:

1,200 calories a day / 5 = 240 calories per meal

1,600 calories a day / 5 = 320 calories per meal

1,800 calories a day / 5 = 360 calories per meal

2,000 calories a day / 5 = 400 calories per meal

I call them meals, but to the standard eye, they may possibly look more like a snack. Please refer back to the tricks I mentioned on the previous page. Satisfaction is in the *brain* of the beholder.

"So what is a calorie anyway, Kate?"

A calorie is a unit of measurement that represents the energy value of food. It's how we measure how much energy it takes our bodies to break down food.

In order for you to avoid extra weight gain, eating more frequently is a must. Continued fuel prevents insulin from skyrocketing, fat cells from plumping, and energy levels from crashing through the floor.

Be kind to your body by taking care of it lovingly. Your body doesn't deserve to be calorie-deprived, binged, purged, or mistreated. Love on this beautiful vessel; your portal to peace, freedom, and living a sexy fit life.

You deserve it. You are ready to embrace this level of self-care.

"What's happening to me? I feel like a hot mess!"

Aah! Hormones. Insulin levels. Withdrawal from toxins in our food. The first week can be a little rough. Plan on it. Journal, hydrate, exercise, talk to your accountability partner. Be sure to stay in touch with your primary doctor throughout the process to ensure all systems are go as you uplevel your life.

As you move through your Inner Hottie transformation, understand that often your emotions will surface as you release old eating habits. Filling this void with self-love, extreme self-care, and deepening relationships with people who support and understand what you are going through, is essential.

And remember, this too shall pass. Your hotness awaits, so stay on task and keep your vision alive and brewing.

HOW TO "CHEAT" ON THE INNER HOTTIE PROGRAM

First, I want to revisit the 90/10 rule. To really get the greatest effect, it is necessary to embrace clean eating 90% of the time.

90% food for fuel.

10% food for enjoyment (within reason).

You gotta' redefine a treat. A treat is NOT a sleeve of Girl Scout cookies.

Plan one or maybe two cheat meals a week. A cheat meal is not an all-you-can-eat smorgasbord. However, if you have a hankering, enjoy one of your favorite foods not on the Clean Eats List. Remember: it's all about portion control. Savor your food and get back on the clean eats train on your next meal. That's it.

You can do it!

Clean Eats Daily Planner

Meal Time example:

Breakfast: 7 a.m.

Mini: 10 a.m.

Lunch: 1 p.m.

Mini: 4 p.m.

Dinner: 6 p.m.

Optional Mini: 8:30 p.m. (with a protein focus)

Kate's Daily Sampling on Her Clean Eats Meal Plan Example

Meal 1

¼ cup dry oatmeal
3 eggs (1 yolk, 3 egg whites or ¾ egg whites)
¼ cup blueberries

Meal 2

12 almonds
1 apple

Meal 3

Ground chicken, turkey, beef on greens, red pepper, 4 oz. sweet or brown rice

Meal 4

Rice cake with 1 tsp. almond butter

Meal 5

Fish or chicken with broccoli and greens with healthy oil dressing

OR a protein shake w/ protein powder, almond milk, and coconut oil

OR unsweetened Greek yogurt

with honey and 12 almonds

OR chicken with green beans or asparagus

OR a protein shake with almond milk

OR ground turkey with green beans and ½ cup brown rice

Feel free, if you are not totally famished after 3 hours, to make the next meal slightly smaller – but whatever you do, please don't skip. Your metabolism will go on slo-mo.

Important: Muscles are metabolically active tissue, which means they use all kinds of calories to keep them all moving and grooving. Muscles are their own fat-burning, calorie-churning machine. The more muscle you have, the hotter and more efficiently you burn. And THAT is a good thing!!

PORTION CONTROL

What Your Plate Should Look Like:

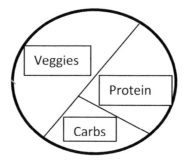

What your plate should not look like:

Kate's Fit Tip: Use smaller plates to help with portion control – and stay away from red dishes. Studies show we eat more on red plates.

Clean Eats Food Preparation

The Ticket to Your Inner Hottie Success

A good offense beats the best defense. Food preparation on the Inner Hottie Program is essential. I spend one hour, three times a week preparing my meals for the days in between and portioning them in containers so I can just grab and go when I leave the house.

Not having the time is not an excuse. If you want to have that sexy sizzle, then your food prep time is a must. Plan it around other activities, invite your family to help, play great music, listen to an audio program, but please commit to this crucial step.

The cleanest fuel of all – self-love and self-acceptance. You got this.

Inner Hottie Clean Eats Summary:

1. Eat more – four to five small meals each day.
2. Eat breakfast – make this meal non-negotiable. Eat within an hour of rising.
3. Eat protein with every meal – eating a lean protein and a complex carbohydrate, at every meal prolongs digestion and encourages stable blood sugars. Make the last meal protein dominate.
4. Eat healthy fats – eat two to three servings of healthy fats every day.
5. Know your portion sizes. Please reference portion size guidelins in this chapter.
6. Prepare your meals in advance – meal preparation is essential for ultimate success.

7. Drink water/stay hydrated – drink no less than 64 ounces of water a day.

Clean Eats + Smaller Plates + Body Moving & Grooving = Hotness!

Remember: Not being properly hydrated causes your metabolism to slow down, meaning you are putting your fat-burning machine on simmer. Glug up the water for furnace-boosting power.

**Hottie Hazard**

Kick your nighttime self-sabotage to the curb.

When is the primary time that diet self-sabotage is most likely to occur?

At night, when defenses are low! Avoid the Inner Hottie saboteur by taking immediate action to put this nasty habit to bed once and for all.

1.Clean out your cabinets. The best offense against this habit is to adopt a great defense – dump the junk. Clear out the refrigerator and cabinets of food that you know will lead to a binge. Not only will you benefit, but so will your entire family.

My last junk clean-eats sweep included stale crackers, fake chocolate peanut butter spread, Oreos, a can of pineapple in heavy syrup and chocolate from last Christmas. Oh my!

Action: Grab a garbage bag and go at this one. It is easy and a quick fix to prevent future diet sabotage.

2.Cut back on screen time. Increased screen time has a direct correlation with a bigger waistline, whether it is due to lack of activity, increased mindless eating, or increased commercial watching leading to junk-food brain programming.

Choose a couple of shows you enjoy, and then turn off the screen as soon as they are over. Cease endless scrolling- set a timer. Learn to savor the food you consume and the company you keep for greater quality of life all around.

Put down your device and find something else to fill your background noise. Try calming music or silence to create a background to your life. Envision how your life will be when you are at your ideal weight and living an active and fit lifestyle. Fill your life with the peace you crave and instead fill your life with the hope of possibility.

3.Dress for success. Choose one piece of exercise/workout wear to put on under your clothes as a continual reminder that you will work out at some time during your day. I always wear an exercise shirt under my dress shirt so that I am ready to go and don't come up with some lame excuse to blow off the gym. On the opposite end of the get dressed for success coin, wear outfits more often that make you feel sexy and confident. Nothing boosts a bad mood than dressing up nice and getting out of the house a bit to re-boot your mindset and socialize in your local community. Share our light. The world needs you!

Part 4
The Inner Hottie Buff Body Plan

4. Thinking back on your childhood, what did you love to do for physical activities? Did it take place inside or outside? With one other person, with a group, or solo?

5. Do you remember being a morning or night person? How about now, what are you?

6. What gave you joy as a child?

7. Where do you remember feeling the most safe and peaceful?

Great job on this. Any cool discoveries for you? Please fill them in here…

"Alright, Kate, this is feeling a little like therapy... Really?... Why does my childhood have anything to do with why I hate to exercise and why I am overweight and out of shape?"

The reason why I ask these questions is that often it is an *inner voice* from our past- something that upended our confidence as a young person, that threw us off track.

This is the work I even do even now as a High Performance Coach because if I can help people tap into what they loved to do previously, it often leads us to the right and perfect path to their biggest ah-ha in their transformative journey.

So what we need to do is remember – remember, so we can set ourselves free from old and outdated thoughts and feelings and become more of who we came to be- a confident and vital human.

Once we set ourselves free from the untruths of the past, and reclaim our innate joy, we can now experience feeling powerful and celebratory in how we show up *today*. It's time to reclaim our rock-star status and live the lives of joy and freedom we deserve.

Now let's translate those positive emotional memories into creating an exercise and movement plan that you will be able to not only commit to but also enjoy. Finding the right exercise plan that fits into your lifestyle is key to getting and keeping your sexy self blazing.

Being Fit is About Living your Joy from the Inside Out.

MODES OF EXERCISE

Please circle any exercises listed below that you would like to incorporate in your daily plan and begin to add some form of exercise into your daily routine.

Here's a partial list of possible *solo* exercise modalities.

walking	treadmill
running	weight lifting
biking	yoga
roller skating	stretching
dancing in your kitchen	stair climbing

Here are some *group* exercise opportunities:

Zumba	running clubs
CrossFit	spinning
aerobics	racquet sports
line dancing	basketball

aerobics	soccer
slow flow yoga	pickle ball

Add your own:

Kate's Inner Hottie Truth

Embracing your Inner Hottie begins with self-love and acceptance at the deepest level. Trust in your inner sanctum where our inner peace resides.

Where is that space for YOU? Where do you feel the deepest level of peace and joy? This feeling is the core of the Inner Hottie journey. Inner confidence and self-awareness are SEXY.

Sure you will have setbacks on your Inner Hottie journey. But view every setback and stumble as opportunities to learn and grow.

I was often criticized for my blind-faith optimism. However, I have come to realize that this "resiliency muscle," as I like to call it, has been the key to my success not only in my fitness journey, but in life.

Staying true to who you are is the magic bullet to living an amazing breakthrough life. Letting go of self-sabotaging habits and beliefs is not easy, but it is so worth it.

I see you soar.

Chapter 18

The Inner Hottie Buff Body Plan

The Five Components of Fitness

"Knowing is not enough: we must apply. Willing is not enough: we must do."

~Goethe

In order to achieve maximum bang for your buck with the Inner Hottie Buff Body Lifestyle Plan, let's dig into the **five components of fitness**. I have found that applying these five elements is crucial to achieving *optimal hotness*.

Your fitness level is defined by how well your body performs in each of these five categories:

1.The Power of the Pillar (Pillar Strength & Flexibility) –The pillar of the body is the foundation from which all movement stems. "Pillar is all the muscles that connect your hips, torso, and shoulders." (M. Verstegen) When these areas are poorly aligned, problems can occur throughout all activities that you engage in.

Think about it – when you twist an ankle, pull your back, or strain a shoulder, your whole movement pattern is affected. Injuries of the elbows and knees are often caused by breaks in movement patterns originating in the pillar. That is why it is so crucial to stay fluid, strong, and flexible in the hip and shoulder areas.

Action: Stretch your hips and shoulders throughout the day. Stand and move around every 30 minutes if you have a sedentary job. Reach your arms out and around, roll your neck, shake out your hips doing circles. Full dance boogie breakout is encouraged!

2.Muscle Flexibility Muscle flexibility is defined as the ability of each and every joint, muscle, and tendon to move through its full range of motion. Exercises that promote flexibility include yoga, Pilates, stretch class, and exercise band work.

As we age, we tend to stretch less, making us more prone to aches and pains, not to mention injury, falls, and strains. Please be the exception to this rule. Keep the body limber and flexible to maintain a youthful and flexible physique.

Action: A healthy muscle is a strong and flexible one. Celebrate moving all of your joints through full range of motion. Smile and sigh as you stretch. Stiffness is a common sensation that needs to be worked through daily to completely unleash your sexy fit. Embrace your ability to move and groove.

3.Muscle Strength Muscle strength describes how much force a muscle can exert. In general, the best way to increase your muscle strength is through strength training – my personal favorite. I view strength training as our own unique ability to play Michelangelo with these beautiful bodies we call our own. All bodies are different; they provide us with unique strategies and challenges to optimize our beautiful machines.

This is the exciting and ever-evolving part of strength training that excites me so much. It has been the reason why I have remained so actively committed to this form of exercise over the last 30 years.

Action: In order to optimize your strength, include strength training in your exercise program. Strength-train for a minimum of three times a week for 30 minutes a session to experience the amazing benefits.

Anyway, given the simple fact that the more muscle you have the more you can eat, I say, heck, why would anyone *not* lift weights??

4.Cardiovascular Health Cardiovascular health describes how well your heart and lungs work together to fuel your body with oxygen to your muscles and how well your muscles use it during sustained physical exertion. We will talk further about the different types of cardio activities in a later chapter, but know that getting the heart and lungs pumping is the best way to get you in that fat-burning zone.

Action: Include daily cardiovascular exercise in your daily routine by "hooking" it to other activities. Carry the laundry upstairs in multiple steps, dance while making dinner, jog to the end of the street before you grab your mail from your mailbox. Include a combination of sustained vigor and bursts of heart-pumping exercise every day. Go for the cardio glow!

5. Body Composition Your body composition serves as a barometer of your overall health and fitness. It takes into consideration your ratio of body fat to lean mass (muscles, bones, and organs) and can be an indicator of possible health risks. Your Inner Hottie goal is to have an optimal lean-tissue-to-body-fat ratio.

Action: The Inner Hottie Buff Body Plan includes both cardiovascular activity and strength training to melt away your body fat and increase muscle mass for greater calorie burn. Having a leaner machine is a great indicator of overall fitness and health, and plus, you just feel better all around.

Chapter 19
The Inner Hottie Buff Body System

Strength-Train Your Way to Hotness and Health
The Benefits of Strength Training

There are no ifs, ands, or buts about it: Strength training is an amazing way to shape your body. The health benefits of pumping weights have been shown over and over again in numerous studies.

Research proves that people who engage in a regular strength training program enjoy a long list of health benefits. Unfortunately, unless we continue to perform regular strength training exercises, we lose more than ½ pound of muscle every year of life after age 25. Yikes!

What does that tell us about our weight gain as so many of us age? Yup, we gain dreaded fat, and at the same time we lose precious muscle. *Now* do you see why I am so passionate about the importance of strength training?

A comprehensive strength training program that addresses all major muscle groups is a great way to prevent injury and degenerative diseases. And nothing will make you feel more sexy than being fit.

Below, I have listed five of the many reasons why you should take strength training more seriously and why now is the time to hop on the iron-pumping bandwagon:

1. *Muscle fights obesity.* The more muscle you have, the more calories you burn, even when you are

sleeping. Each pound of muscle actually burns an extra 35 to 50 calories a day. A pound of fat burns only 2 calories a day. Yucko! Bring on the muscle!

2. *Strength training increases overall strength and energy for daily activities.* Weight training increases spinal bone density in as little as six months of training, thereby preventing osteoporosis.

3. *Strength training reduces risk of diabetes and heart disease.* Studies show that strength training increases glucose/blood sugar utilization by approximately 25% in four months. Also, stronger muscles lead to a stronger heart and decrease the risk of heart attack and heart disease.

4. *Strength training fights back pain and arthritis.* Lifting weights reduces chronic pain. It increases muscle strength, making us more able to stand and move in correct posture and alignment, and makes us more readily able to perform daily activities pain-free.

5. *Strength training reduces depression and anxiety.* A Harvard study found that 10 weeks of strength training reduced clinical depression symptoms. You just feel more confident and capable after a workout, and that translates into a happier state of being.

Certainly the health benefits are well documented. From my own personal experience, nothing in my life has made me feel more centered and powerful than the experience of a great workout.

Do I personally always love my exercise sessions? Nope. But do I like the way it makes me look and feel? Heck, yeah. It is the main reason why I am so passionate about inspiring others to be fit: So that they too can experience the amazing feelings of being in complete flow with their bodies and of being both strong and powerful.

Be ready to see your body change in ways that will surprise you. Notice how your inner confidence shifts. Observe how your stress level decreases. Be ready for your sex drive to increase. Trust me here. These things really do happen. I used to hear it all the time from my fitness clients.

Strength Training 101
The Inner Hottie Way

For maximum results, and to prevent injury, please follow these guidelines as you work through your strength training program:

1. *Warm Up.* "Cold muscles" are more susceptible to injury. Start your workout session with light aerobic activity, such as a few minutes on the treadmill or light calisthenics like jumping jacks, arm circles, toe touches, or *dynamic stretches* that loosen the muscles.

2. *Focus on Form.* Correct form is crucial to prevent injury and to attain maximum gains when lifting weights. It is important to perform each exercise through a full range of motion, emphasizing the "squeeze" in the muscle at maximum contraction.

Don't rush. Working through the whole range of motion reaps the greatest benefits.

3. *Use Enough Resistance.* Nothing drives me crazier than seeing someone lift a 2-lb. weight when they can manage two to three times that weight at least! Your goal in your strength training program is to work the targeted muscle to fatigue. Lift the appropriate amount of weight to challenge your body for optimal hotness. I know you want the gains. It is time for you to go after them.

4. *Listen to your Body.* Breathe, stretch between sets, tune in to how your body is feeling. Pay attention to pinches or strains. Notice where you feel tight and stiff, and use your weight training time to work through these tight areas. Stay tuned in to your form for maximum benefit. And if something hurts or pulls, please stop that exercise and move onto another. Respect what your body tells you, but always continue to challenge your body past its previous plateau.

5. *Push through Fear and Resistance.* This is probably the stickiest point for newbies as they start to lift weights. The key is this: the body will follow what the mind sets out to do. Believe that you can make the gains you desire, and your body will follow suit. Sometimes you reach a point where your mind will try to psych you out and you will doubt your ability to move heavier weights. It is important to visualize yourself going through the exercise, breathe and dig in. You will be in awe of how quickly they improve when you fully commit to the best version of you. Trust and believe.

Strength Training Guidelines
(Boring, but Important)

When performing your strength training workout, please consider the following guidelines:

1. *Exercise Selection:* Select at least one exercise for each major muscle group to ensure that your muscle development is balanced. Please consult the exercises in Chapter 22.
2. *Exercise Sequence:* Vary your exercise sequencing when performing your workout.
   Oftentimes, we work from larger to smaller muscle groups starting with the larger muscle groups (chest, back, quadriceps, hamstrings, glutes) and work the smaller muscle groups after (biceps/triceps, calves); or we can switch things up by working upper and lower body in different workouts on different days.
3. *Exercise Sets and Repetitions:* A set is defined as a number of "reps" (repetitions) performed of a given exercise. In the Inner Hottie plan, you will start by performing each series of exercises for one or two sets. Performing three sets of each exercise is for the more advanced Buff Body Babe. Go at your own pace and work up gradually in the number of sets you perform to avoid injury and risk overtraining.
4. *Exercise Progression:* The key to experiencing strength gains is applying "progressive resistance" to your exercise program. Once a muscle adapts to a certain amount of resistance, you will need to switch things up to keep the body guessing. For example,

an ideal rep range in a set is lifting the weight between 8 and 12 times. When you can perform 12 reps with relative ease, it is time to increase the weight that you are lifting by about 5%. To make the gains, keep your body in "shock and awe." Just as in our intimate relationships, it is important to keep things fresh by switching things up. This same principle applies to your gym time as it does to the bedroom.

Chapter 20

The Inner Hottie Buff Body Cardio System

Cardiovascular Exercise – Go for the Glow

When starting <u>any</u> exercise program, it is recommended that you make an appointment with your doctor to get the go-ahead on moving forward on your lifestyle changes and fitness goals.

Cardiovascular health is a crucial element of the Inner Hottie Lifestyle Plan. We must get the heart pumping to fully elevate our hotness factor!

The benefits of performing cardiovascular exercise include:

- decreased blood pressure
- improved glucose tolerance
- reduced anxiety
- decreased risk of cardiovascular disease and diabetes
- increased vitality and elevated mood
- increased sex drive
- better sleep

As you can see, being in good cardiovascular health is the foundation of your fitness program and a crucial element in your overall health and your ability to enjoy your life, from playing with your kids to the ease at which you tackle your everyday tasks to even having a more fulfilling sex life.

The Components of a Cardiovascular Work-Out

When we talk about taking cardiovascular exercise, we are referring to how well our heart, lungs, and circulatory system work together for optimal health and glow.

There are four elements that make up a rocking cardio plan, including:

- mode
- frequency
- duration
- Intensity

Let's start from the top.

Mode: When we talk of our mode in our cardio program, we are talking about what cardio we will perform based on our interest, availability of time, and availability of equipment, and on our fitness goals. It is necessary that we figure out what will personally work for us so we can ensure that we will stay committed to the Inner Hottie Plan. Don't choose the elliptical if you absolutely hate it. Being able to adhere to your mode of exercise and being clear on what you like and don't like is key.

Frequency: Frequency is deciding how many cardio sessions you are going to do each week. The American College of Sports Medicine recommends that we perform at least three to five days a week for most aerobic activities. In the Inner Hottie program, we focus on getting back to basics, incorporating more movement *each and every day*, and incorporating a more structured cardio session into our exercise regimen several times a week.

My questions to you when we talk about frequency are, "Are you committed to being Sexy Fit? To finally lose the extra fat that weighs you down? To embrace a more joy-filled lifestyle and feeling sexier and more vibrant?" If you are saying "yes, yes!" to these challenges, then it is time for you to commit to doing your cardio with more frequency so as to attain the body you desire. You are worth it.

Duration: Duration refers to the number of minutes you perform your cardiovascular exercise in one session. Beginners, those who are just introducing or reintroducing more cardio and movement in their lives, should begin with 10- to 15-minute sessions. Intermediate fitness babes should be working up to the 40- to 60-minute zone, for maximum fat burn. Listen to your body. Reduce the length of cardio you are performing if you suddenly feel dizzy or experience lightheadedness.

Intensity: Intensity measures the speed or the workload of the exercise you are performing. The American College of Sports Medicine recommends an intensity range of 55% to 90% of maximum heart rate. The wide variable in this range highlights the importance of your consulting with your physician for a full checkup. I also recommend meeting with a fitness professional, who can perform a fitness assessment on you to determine a recommended level of exertion during your cardiovascular exercise and strength training program.

These professionals will be able to take into consideration your body composition, your age, your overall health, and any health risks and/or injuries to create an ideal cardio target exertion goal.

Keeping your focus on the intensity of your exercise means staying intentional to your goals *even* and *especially* when you don't feel like it. And if this isn't your first round on the fitness and health rodeo, those times do come.

Be prepared by staying clear in your goals and keeping up the intensity of your commitment to maximize your gains. Woo hoo!

Monitoring Exercise Intensity the Inner Hottie Way

As a previous fitness professional, I most often monitor my clients' levels of exertion and how hard to push them based on what we the industry calls the **"talk test."** By paying attention to how my clients were breathing and how quickly they recovered, I could pace their workouts accordingly. You can do the same thing for yourself.

Paying attention to your breathing is a great way for you to tune in to your own workouts. More on this when we talk about Borg's Rate of Exertion below.

Another method of measuring exertion is the **Training Heart Rate Method.** This is calculated by subtracting your age from 220. Your training heart rate (THR) is your maximum measured heart rate multiplied by 60% to 90%.

For example: A 40-year-old woman for whom an intensity of 70% maximum heart rate is desired:

220
- 40 (age)

= 180 (predicted maximum heart rate)

x 70% or 0.70

= 126 (targeted exercise heart rate)

So as she is performing her cardio, 126 beats per minute would be her targeted rate for maximum benefit at 70% of maximum intensity. You can calculate your own THR by using the above formula.

Another way of measuring your own exertion is with **Borg's Rating of Perceived Exertion (RPE)**, my personal favorite and the method I most frequently taught my clients.

Borg Rating of Perceived Exertion (RPE)
The Inner Hottie Way

Level 1: I am watching TV, eating Cheetos.

Level 2: I am comfortable and could maintain this pace all day.

Level 3: I am still comfortable, but I am breathing just a bit harder.

Level 4: I am sweating a little, but I feel good and can carry on a conversation effortlessly.

Level 5: I am just above comfortable, sweating more, and can still talk with relative ease.

Level 6: I can still talk, but I am slightly breathless.

Level 7: I can still talk, but I don't really want to. I am sweating.

Level 8: I can grunt in response to your questions and can keep this pace for only a short time.

Level 9: I think I am dying. Gasp!

Level 10: What happened? Overexertion!

For maximum benefit in your cardio and exercise routine, play in levels 5 to 8.

It is crucial as you embrace your fitness journey that you take responsibility for your health and monitor your efforts to be sure you are not under-challenging yourself as much as you are not over-challenging yourself.

Being overzealous certainly is dangerous when exercising, because it does increase your chance of injury; however, under-challenging yourself is also an issue with people as well.

This happens for a variety of reasons:

- fear of pain
- feeling self-conscious
- dislike of sweating
- fear of wrecking our hair-do (truth)
- fear of success
- even fear of extreme hurt or death

Seriously, these fears and emotions are real. As coaches, whether we are talking about working with the mind or body, we understand the fine line of resistance in how far to push our clients just enough to achieve their goals. It is a tricky dance for sure and makes the work so exciting!

And so I get it that it's sometimes difficult to know just how hard to push yourself, but I encourage you to just keep walking to your edge and try to go a little farther, a little harder each time. This is where our biggest breakthroughs will happen- guaranteed.

Variety Is the Spice of Life
Different Aerobic Training Methods the Inner Hottie Way

Let's talk about three different aerobic training methods that you can use to get your game on and get your buff body moving and grooving. They are continuous training, interval training, and circuit training.

Continuous Aerobic Training is when your intensity remains between 50% and 85% of functional capacity (5 to 8 on Borg's scale). Shoot for 20 to 60 minutes as the ideal for maximum fitness improvement and body fat reduction. Remember that the intensity needs to be enough to get you in that fat-burning zone, so stay tuned in to your breathing and play at the higher end of your exertion scale for more effective gains.

Interval Training or HIIT TRAINING (high-intensity interval training) combines higher and lower levels of intensity throughout a cardio session. An example of this style of training is a spinning class or varied intervals on the treadmill, elliptical, bike, or track.

HIIT training has been shown to be very effective at increasing your metabolic rate; however, because of the greater intensity, it is important that you receive clearance from your doctor before you take on this style of conditioning.

Perform HIIT initially for a 10-minute session, then move to a minimum of 20 minutes and a maximum of 40 minutes to get your heart pumping and your metabolic rate churning.

Circuit Training is a great method of exercise that produces quicker gains by moving through a series of exercises with relatively brief rest periods between each station.

The cool thing about circuit training is that you can use strength training and cardio stations in combination, or a variety of cardiovascular exercises, in a single session to mix things up and keep the body guessing for maximum benefit and fitness gains.

Example of a Cardio/Strength Sequence:

Warmup on treadmill: 5 minutes
Body-weight squats: 1 minute (AMAP – as many as possible)
Treadmill: 5 minutes
Push Ups on bench: 1 minute (AMAP)
Treadmill: 5 minutes
Ab crunches: 1 minute (AMAP)
Complete.

You can repeat this cycle two to three times. Feel free to change up the cardio modality. Choose exercises from Chapter 22 of this book.

Example of Cardio Circuit Only:

Treadmill: 5 minutes
Stationary bike: 5 minutes
Elliptical: 5 minutes

Complete!

For an intermediate workout, repeat this cycle two to three times for maximum fat-burning and metabolism-boosting gain.

As you can see, there are many ways to shake things up when you embrace the Inner Hottie Buff Body Lifestyle Plan. As with anything in life, it is important to switch things up to keep your body and mind guessing. To me, this is way more fun than a Sudoku puzzle.

Not only does change-up prevent boredom to set in, but it is also crucially important in making the quickest gains.

Kate Gets Real...

Those who know me know that cardio is not my favorite! It's the truth. But in order to be in optimal health, and because heart disease runs in my family, I have come to embrace cardiovascular exercise.

I have found ways that work for me so I can perform this exercise mode with greater ease and less angst. What I have chosen to do is add more cardio bursts throughout my day: a brisk 15-minute walk with my pup, an extra set of stairs as I bring laundry up and down, a sprint to the mailbox, a longer treadmill warm-up before my weight training session. This works for me.

What will work for you? Investigate what you like to do (or can tolerate) and make a plan to get your body in action.

Cardio Health = Increased Stamina = Less Fatigue = Less Injury = More Fun!

Exercise Tips to Remember:

- *Stop exercising immediately when you experience chest discomfort, numbing of limbs, light-headedness, or dizziness.*
- *Reduce exercise intensity in very hot or humid conditions.*
- *Avoid exercise with pain in a joint that only gets worse as you exercise.*
- *If you are under the care of a doctor for a chronic medical condition, obtain clearance from the doctor before proceeding with this or any exercise program.*

Hottie Hazard

"I don't have time to warm up. I am just going to go all out in this exercise class or weight training program."

Please don't! It is crucial that you gradually increase your heart rate, your blood pressure, your oxygen consumption, and the elasticity of your muscles and joints to prevent injury and health risks. Be kind to your body. Warm it up with care.

Chapter 21

The Claim Your Inner Hottie Motivational Mojo and Exercise

It's not about *finding* time; it's about *making* time!

Tips to Making the Time to Work Out

1. *Pack your workout bag the night before.* Truth: I have been known to wear my workout clothes to bed. Also, if I know I won't be hitting the gym until the end of the day, I will wear one piece of clothing that is fitness-related under my clothes, even if it is just my sports bra, to remind myself of my commitment to my fit time.

2. *Pack your pre-workout meal/snack the night before*, so you can grab it and go in the morning. Have you ever said to yourself, "I will just stop at home and grab something to eat," and found yourself in your pajamas in front of the TV covered in Doritos dust three hours later? Be prepared and avoid this serious Hottie Hazard.

3. *Plan on it!* Set your workout schedule for the week and stick to it. Make a commitment to your best and highest Sexy Fit self. For real, the weight-loss/get-fit journey is not an easy one; if it were, we would all be buff. Rid yourself of roadblocks that prevent you from getting to the gym by making this date with yourself non-negotiable.

4. *Find an accountability pal.* This is so crucial to your success. Share your Inner Hottie Commitment Contract with a trusted coach or friend and be sure to tell WHY you want to achieve these goals. Remember: The WHY is the firewood in your furnace of attaining your dreams.

5. *Get more done in less time with HIIT training.* The trend is toward shorter and more intense exercise sessions for a quicker fat burn and metabolism boost. The whole idea of HIIT training is to keep the body's fat-consuming furnace on high and put demands on the body to keep it guessing what is next. You can do this in a couple of different ways:

   a. Perform cardio in bursts at high intensity for, say, 30 seconds, then slow down until your heart rate drops back to a light jog rate, then boost it up for 30 to 50 seconds, repeating this for 25 to 30 minutes four to five times a week.

   b. Combine the cardio component with weights to really jack up your cardio and muscle-building machine. For example, perform 1 minute of cardio equipment followed by 20 squats, then go back to the cardio for 1 to 2 minutes at a high-intensity pace, then do a barbell chest press and then go back to the cardio component, repeating this process for 20 to 30 minutes. Mix it up for maximum fat-burning, muscle-building fun!

Chapter 22

The Claim Your Inner Hottie Exercise Program

Perfect Posture:

The proper stance for optimal movement. Shoulder blades are back and down. The tummy is drawn up and in, activating the core muscles. Imagine a straight line from the ears to the shoulders, from the shoulders to the hips, from the hips to the knees, and from the knees to the ankles. Energy is rising out the top of your head.

Practice in front of the mirror first with your eyes open, and then try it with your eyes closed. Incorporate this long and lean vision all day long.

Athletic Stance:

The proper form for all sport and lifestyle movement. Start with holding perfect posture. Keep your legs slightly bent, with your bootie sitting slightly back and down. The weight is toward the front of the feet. Your core is engaged.

You are ready to roll!

Suitcase Squats

1. Holding a dumbbell in each hand, stand in perfect posture, with your shoulder blades down and back, chest lifted, and core engaged.
2. Slowly bring the weights down toward the floor, keeping the chest lifted and shifting the weight back on your heels, your glutes sticking out and back.
3. As you come up, keep the chest lifted and your weight on the heels. At the top, give the glutes a good squeeze. Repeat.

Sumo Plie Squats

1. Step out into a wide stance with your feet turned out, parallel to your knees. Rotate out only as far as you are comfortable.
2. While holding a dumbbell with two hands, slowly lower down into a plié, keeping the weight distribution toward your heels. Do not let your knees rotate in.
3. When you are coming back up, activate the glutes, imagining energy coming out the top of your head. Give the glutes a squeeze at the top. Repeat.

Lunges (with dumbbells)

1. Standing in perfect posture, with your shoulders back and down, dumbbells by your side, step out with the left foot with a wide but comfortable step.
2. While you're in this posture, be sure your body weight is on the heel of the front foot, bend the back knee, lowering your body down until you feel a stretch in the front hamstring. Be sure the front knee does not pass the foot.
3. Lift your body up and back to the start position, pushing up and away and back to standing position, feet together. Repeat, leading with the other leg.

Deadlift (Hamstring and Glutes)

1. Start with the dumbbells facing your thighs, your knees slightly bent, your chest lifted, and your core engaged.
2. As you breathe in, slowly lower the weights toward the floor, keeping the weights close to the body and keeping your back straight. You should feel a stretch in the back of the legs.
3. Once you have reached as low as you can go, feeling a nice stretch in the hamstrings, blow out as you squeeze your glutes and bring the weights up alongside your legs. Be sure the weight is on the heels.

> TIP:
> Keep the weight on
> the heels of the feet.

Calf Raises

1. Stand on one leg. Hold onto a steady object for balance.
2. Slowly lift up onto your toe to full extension, blowing out as you rise. Then slowly lower yourself with a controlled movement. Repeat.

Variation: You can also try this holding a dumbbell in your free hand.

Pushups (Chest, Triceps)

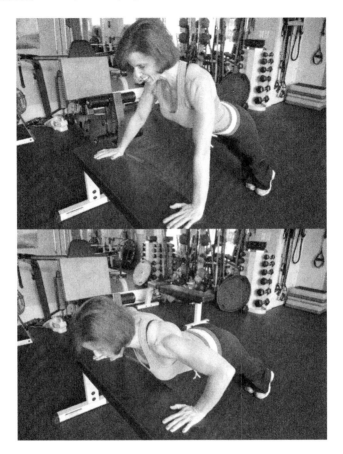

1. Start by placing your hands slightly wider apart than your shoulders on a bench, counter, or chair. Walk your feet out so that you are in a plank position as shown in position 1 above.
2. With your core activated and with energy coming out of your head, slowly lower your chest to the bench.
3. Slowly press with the palms of the hands and blow out as you push your chest away from the bench. Repeat.

Dumbbell Press (Chest)

1. Lie on a bench with the dumbbells by your chest, creating a V with each arm, feeling a nice stretch through the shoulders and chest.
2. While breathing out, push the dumbbells up until your arms are essentially extended above your chest (level with your nipples). Slowly lower the weights down as you breathe in.

> TIPS:
> Don't over-grip the dumbbells.
> Keep your hips planted on bench.

Dumbbell Flyes (Chest)

1. Lying flat on the bench, hold the dumbbells above your chest so they are touching each other and your arms are extended but bent, as if you are hugging a barrel.
2. Inhale as you lower the weights to either side; your arms will remain fixed in their barrel-hugging angle, and the weights will arc outward as they come down. Be careful not to bring the dumbbells too low. Now, breathing out, return to the start position.

> TIP:
> Keep the chest lifted and slightly arch your back.

<u>Bent-Over Dumbbell Rows</u>

1. While standing in your athletic stance, bend at the hips with the dumbbells in front of you, facing each other.
2. As you breathe in, bring the dumbbells up and back along your body, elbows lifting, chest lifted.

> TIP:
> Keep your face and chest open and up, and your core activated.

Dumbbell Military Press (Shoulders)

1. To begin, lift the dumbbell over and above your shoulders with the elbows bent, again forming V's with your arms.
2. As you blow out, lift the weights in a semicircle over your head with a smooth movement. Lower the weight to the start position in a controlled pace with your chest lifted.

```
TIPS:
Keep your chest lifted. Be careful
not to over-grip the weights.
```

<u>Lateral Raises</u> (Shoulders)

1. Hold the dumbbells at your hips facing in, your elbows and knees slightly bent. Bend slightly forward at the waist. You are in the athletic stance.

2. As you breathe out, raise the weights out to the side, imagining that you are holding two pitchers in each hand. As you raise the weight, pretend that you are pouring something out of the pitchers at the top phase of the repetition. Breathe in as you lower the weights.

TIP:
Keep your knees slightly bent through this exercise, and your core engaged.

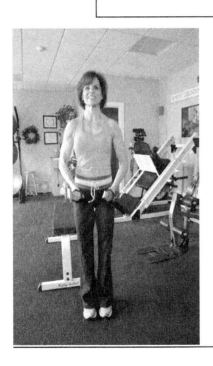 

Rear Bent Raises (Shoulders)

1. Sit on the bench, holding the dumbbells facing each other underneath your legs, keeping your elbows slightly bent.
2. Pressing your chest forward into your knees, lift the weights up and out, keeping the elbows slightly bent, blowing out on exertion.

> TIP:
> Use the same pitcher-pouring technique you do on the lateral raises.

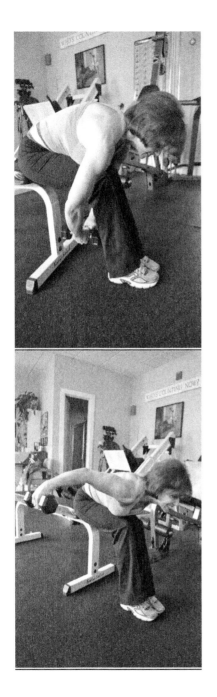

149

Triceps Dumbbell Kickbacks

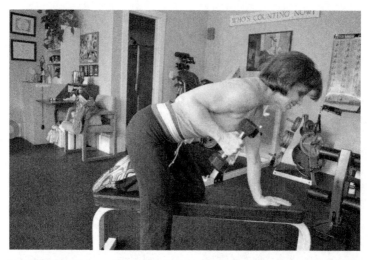

1. Start with one knee and the corresponding palm on the bench.
2. With a dumbbell in the opposite hand and the corresponding elbow pressed into your side, extend your arm straight back and squeeze the muscle in the back of your arm. Repeat.

Keep your core activated and your back straight throughout the exercise.

Bench Dips (Triceps)

1. Start out sitting on the edge of the bench with your fingers facing your body. Lift your booty off the bench as you walk your feet out a comfortable distance.
2. As you breathe in, lower your body along the bench, keeping your elbows in and back.
3. Once you have reached your full depth, blow out as you press up, straightening your arms.

> TIP:
> Remember to keep your body close to the bench as you do this exercise.

Dumbbell Curls (Biceps)

1. Hold the dumbbells by your side, weights along your body.
2. As you blow out, raise the weights up toward your shoulders, being aware of the contraction in the biceps.
3. Blow out as you lower the weights in a controlled and smooth motion.

TIP:
Be careful not to over-grip weights.

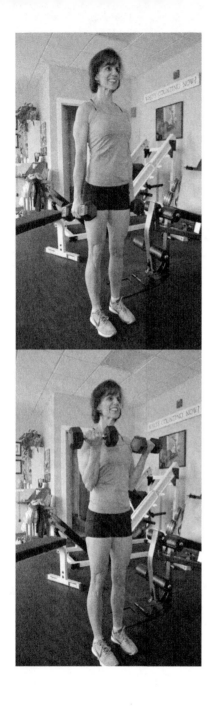

1. Start this exercise lying flat on your back and holding a light dumbbell overhead. As you blow out, lift your body slightly up off the mat. Imagine that your core is being scooped out like a scoop of gelato. Pause for two counts at the top of the exercise.
2. Lower the weight slowly back and away, with a slight bend in the elbow.

1. With your fingers gently resting on the back of your head and your elbows pressing out, slowly lift the chest up and out until you feel the core activating, particularly on the upper part of the abdomen, just below the ribs.

2. Keeping the elbows pressed back, lower your body to the mat, keeping the core activated throughout the up-and-down movement.

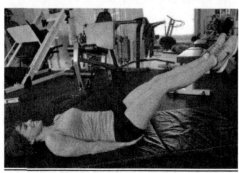

1. Lying flat on your back, rest your hands under your glutes, palms facing down, with your legs up and slightly bent.
2. Slowly lower the legs down toward the floor, contracting the lower abs. Lower your legs only as low as is comfortable, being cautious that you put no stress on the lower back.
3. Breathe in as you bring your legs back up to position 1. Repeat.

Chest Stretch

With the core activated and one shoulder blade back and down, grip a post with your hand and stretch away, feeling a great stretch in the shoulder and chest. Repeat with your other arm.

Lat Stretch

With the core active, grasp a pole and, with soft knees, lean your body away, feeling a great stretch through the upper back and rear shoulder.

Shoulder Stretch

Either sitting or standing, grasp the opposing elbow with the opposite hand and pull the elbow back, bending slightly at the waist to intensify the stretch. Repeat on the other side.

Side Stretch 1

Breathe in deeply as you reach one arm up and over your head, feeling a stretch from the hip all the way through the armpit and blow out as you lean fully into the stretch. Repeat on the other side.

Hip Stretch 1

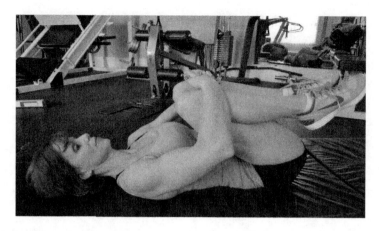

Lying flat on your back, gently bring your hips into your chest and hold for a count of 10. With each breath in and out, feel the hips release a little more. Rock gently back and forth, come to center, and then release the knees to the floor. Feel the weight of your body resting into the mat.

Hip Stretch 2

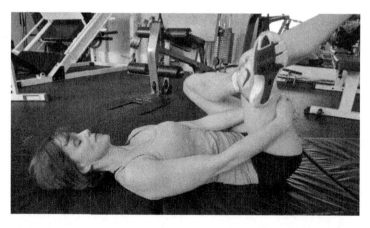

Lying on your back, rest one ankle on the opposing knee. Grasp behind the thigh and, blowing in and out, pull the leg toward the chest. You should feel the stretch in the hip and outer thigh of the crossed leg.

Hip Stretch 3

Lying on your back, gently bring one knee to the chest, imagining you are creating more space in that hip joint. Hold for 10 seconds. Rock slightly to the left and right. Release and rotate to the other side.

Hip Stretch 4

Lying flat on your back, bring one knee up and then gently drop the knee across the body, keeping the shoulder blades pressing into the mat. Focus on your breath, and feel the waist and hip open and release. Bring the leg back to center, lower the leg, and perform the stretch on the other side.

Hip Stretch 5

Sit with one leg straight out behind you and one leg bent in front, using your hands to monitor the intensity of the hip stretch. Breathe in and out, allowing the hip to release deeper with each breath. Repeat with the leg positions reversed.

Hip Stretch 6a

Hip Stretch 6b

1. Start with the legs a comfortable width apart in a sitting position. You can also perform this stretch with your back against a wall for extra support. Be sure that your feet are rotated slightly out and in line with your knees.
2. Breathing in, lift your arms up overhead and activate the core. Slowly bring your arms in front of you toward the floor, resting your fingertips for support. Breathe in and out as you feel the release in the hips. Move the fingers a little to the left and right to expand on the stretch.
3. Slowly walk your fingers in and raise your body up, then bring the legs together and shake them out. Repeat one to two times.

Inner Thigh Stretch 1

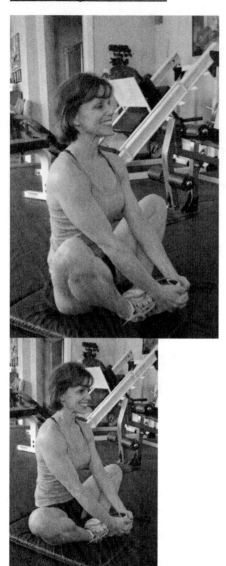

1. Sitting on the mat, bring the soles of your feet together and activate your core, keeping the shoulders back and down, chest lifted.
2. As you breathe out, lower the knees toward the mat. You can use the palms of the hands on the inside of the knees to increase the stretch. Repeat.

Inner Thigh Stretch 2

1. Sitting on the mat with your legs in front of you, bring one knee up and over the other knee.
2. Wrap the opposite arm around the knee and, with the free arm, reach around and rest your fingers on the mat.
3. Breathe in as you lift the chest and rotate the rib cage, feeling a great stretch in the hip and waist. Blow out all your breath when you reach the full stretch, hold, then release. Repeat on the opposite side, noticing how the stretch may feel different on each side. Breathe into any tight areas.

Hamstring Stretch 1-3

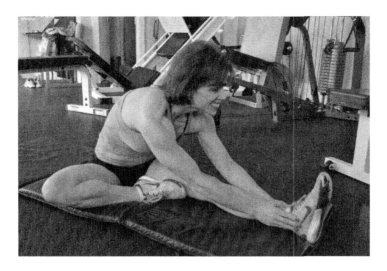

1. Sitting with both legs in front of you, lift the arms overhead as you breathe in.
2. As you release your breath, lean forward, imagining energy coming out of the top of your head. Do not slump into the stretch, and keep your core active.

Variation: bend one leg with the foot against the inside of the knee and hinge at your waist. Again, notice the difference, if any, in each hip. Breathe into any tight spots.

Part 5
Putting the Plan into Action

Chapter 23

Living the Inner Hottie Lifestyle– Putting It All Together

Are you ready to put it all together?

As we discussed throughout this book, being truly fit requires a holistic approach by incorporating the mind, body, and soul of who you are at the deepest level and bringing all your good to the surface.

But first, in order to life with greater vitality and confidence, it's time for you to get real and get radical about what you will expect out of this opportunity before you. And frankly, isn't it due time you gave your negative self-talk and unhealthy habits the boot?

By embracing the Inner Hottie Lifestyle Plan, be prepared for your life to change, possibly in all areas and facets. Expecting the shake-up will help you stay focused and committed to your highest and best kick-butt self, by being crystal clear on what you want, why you want it and having others who love you to support you on your journey.

I hear it all the time from clients, even friends: "Well Kate, you are just different, most people cannot do what you do, with the same passion, drive and desire." And my response is, "Are we talking about all these other people, or are we talking about you?" Why is it that when we feel like we cannot attain something we start talking about ourselves in the third person, the mysterious "other"?

So I ask you this: How bad do you want it? How bad do you want to feel more confident and sexy? How bad do you want to have deeper and more meaningful relationships? How bad do you want to live with passion and financial abundance and a deep conviction that there is more than enough? How bad do you want to be free from self-sabotage and feelings of negative self-worth?

If you have read this far, then gosh darn it, you want it pretty bad, and I too want you to have all that you desire. And this is the core reason why I have written *Claim Your Inner Hottie*: to inspire and challenge you to grow through emotional blocks and truly "see" yourself as the whole and healthy Hottie that you came here to be.

The truth is I will not let you settle for less than you deserve or desire. It is the success stories of my clients that drive me on a daily basis. To inspire you to have the courage and faith to live your life all out, with passion, confidence, and a sexy sizzle!

The first step is to set yourself free from negative self-talk and personal soul bashing. It is possible, I promise you, to be free of this self-defeating behavior. The biggest success will come to those who are finally ready to shift their self-perception, become aware of self-defeating language and behavior, and move into a place of positive self-worth and self-love. Positive mojo is a choice. Live it.

The second step of the Inner Hottie challenge is incorporating and embracing the clean eats diet program. By eating clean, you will become so in tune with your body, it will blow you away. Once you make the change to a healthy lifestyle, it is nearly impossible to turn back. You will see clearly that the best way to honor yourself is to honor the body you have been given to the highest level. You deserve it.

And lastly, by incorporating the Inner Hottie Buff Body exercise plan, you will be able to create killer results and a chiseled physique by being your own Michelangelo. I believe there is no better way to have a shapely physique than to incorporate strength training.

Also by getting on a regular cardio plan, you will be able to see fat fall away and your health increase on all levels. And there is nothing sexier than the just-exercised glow.

Please do not cut yourself short. I want you to succeed, and I will do all that I can to ensure that this becomes a reality. I am here cheering you on every step of the way.

My Inner Hottie Tribe, I look forward to that day when we can meet each other and you can tell me all about your transformation.

I look forward to us doing the happy dance together!

In celebration of your courage, strength, and willingness to go all in and lots, and lots of love,

Kate

Kate McKay

High Performance Coach

www.kate-mckay.com

FAQs

"How long will it take to see results?"

When you begin to follow the Inner Hottie Lifestyle of eating clean and exercise, you will find almost immediately that you have increased energy and a healthy glow. As for weight loss, if that is your goal, each person will experience a different rate due to variations such as overall health, genetics, amount of exercise output, and commitment to eating clean.

Plan on losing 1½ to 2 lbs. per week on average, with some weeks more than others.

"I don't think I can eat this much food."

I get it! But trust me, when you are eating the Inner Hottie Clean Eats way, you will be shocked how your body burns and churns all the yummy fuel. Your energy will be more consistent, and your vibrancy will go through the roof. Count on it.

Feel free, if you are not totally famished after 2½ to 3 hours, to make the next meal slightly smaller – but whatever you do, please don't skip. Your metabolism will go on slo-mo.

"How can I avoid midlife weight gain muffin top?"

- Eat breakfast.
- Exercise regularly, doing both cardio and weights.
- Eat enough protein.
- Get a good night's sleep.
- Avoid alcohol.
- Drink lots of water.

- Limit stress.

"Cripes, Kate. You eat all the time. How come??"

The ticket to being Sexy Fit is to embrace grazing. Studies show that eating more frequently each day keeps the metabolism elevated; as a result, you will burn more calories throughout the day. Choose healthy lean proteins and vegetables as your primary meal sources, and eat moderate amounts of fruit and healthy fats to keep you going.

"Should I eat before I work out?"

For most, starting your workout with something in your tank is key. To perform optimally, fuel your muscles in the hour before hitting the gym with a 150- to 250-calorie snack. Try a rice cake with a tablespoon of natural peanut butter, or a half cup of low-fat cottage cheese with 6 to 12 almonds, or a Granny Smith apple with a tablespoon of almond butter. A double chocolate doughnut is not considered a healthy snack. The body needs fuel to perform at its best.

"What is D.O.M.S?"

DOMS stands for delayed-onset muscle soreness, or what I call the "36-hour rule." After a vigorous workout, your muscles have depleted their glycogen store. Also during your workout, your muscles experience micro-trauma to the muscle fibers. As a result, muscle soreness ensues. How sore you are depends on the intensity and duration of your workout, your hormone levels, and how well your tank is fueled. It is imperative that, after completing a vigorous workout, you hydrate, eat healthy, and rest to allow the body to recover.

Maximize your benefits by giving the body what it needs for restoration. Make your restoration time **as important as your workouts. Some may call it extreme self-care. I call it smart living**

"What's all the buzz about yoga?"

Yoga is thousands of years old but is still a new concept for many of us. There are many different practices of yoga, so if you are interested in taking a class, be sure that you ask what method of yoga is taught and what the teacher's credentials are. Make the teacher aware of your injuries or limitations so she can offer posture modifications. Start slowly and be gentle with yourself. A flexible body is a strong body, and yoga is a wonderful way to increase your flexibility, thereby reducing your chance of injury. Yoga is also great for increasing body awareness, reducing stress, and connecting the mind and the body. Studies show that you can achieve greater results in your workouts through visualization of specific muscles. This mind/body connection will improve your workouts and benefit other phases of your life. I believe that by connecting to the body, great things can happen.

"Will I look like a man? I won't get too big, will I? I don't want to get bulky."

Over the past 20 years, I have been weight training, I have heard those questions and statements over and over again. And the answer is a resounding NO!

Research has shown over and over that women who engage in a regular strength training program enjoy a long list of health benefits. As you realize the advantages of strength training and start feeling the effects of increased vitality, your doubts and fears of "bulking up" will rapidly fade.

Best of luck on your Inner Hottie journey!

ABOUT THE AUTHOR

Kate McKay is living proof that every single one of us is capable of overcoming adversity and living the most amazing life we can imagine. Despite experiencing the worst tragedy of a parent, the loss of her son in 2017, Kate continues to be a positive force of inspiration for others; she is deeply committed to helping her audiences and clients overcome adversity by providing actionable tools to live a fulfilling and meaningful life.

Kate continued her study in Theater at Bennington College and found her deeper passion for fitness and wellness here. Kate believes that this passion for health helped her get through the tragic loss of her brother to murder when she was 23.

Enthusiastic living has always been Kate's MO; her hunger for knowledge and desire to share what she learns to help others to be their best has always been her driving force in life. Being a mom was a natural extension of this, and Kate embraced this role with her three children wholeheartedly.

At age 41, however, Kate found herself overweight, out of shape, and deeply sad. She felt stuck in a financially strapped and unhappy marriage. Her lack of confidence hit an all-time low. One day, after dragging herself to the gym, she looked in the mirror and realized that no one would rescue her from her mess but her. She committed to re-write her story and reclaim her life. With the support of a couple of great coaches, she did just that.

McKay accepted this personal mission to get into the best shape of her life. At 43, she entered and won her first bikini competition. Kate continued to compete in several competitions through the age of 54. In addition, to conquer her scarcity mentality and create a financially stable home for her children and her future. Kate started and built a multi-million dollar business out of her home, even though she had never taken a single business class.

In 2017, tragedy struck Kate's life once again with the suicide of her son Will. As painful as this was, Kate realized that she needed to use her public influence as an author, speaker, and coach to be a messenger of healing and growth for others. This loss has instilled faith and confidence in her purpose and passion that fuels her every day to be a conduit of hope and strength for others. Kate believes this is her legacy and lives in this clarity in her every waking hour.

McKay's desire to inspire and motivate others has resulted in the continued growth of her speaking, coaching practice, and helping others build an amazing life. She hopes to inspire change from the inside out by providing actionable tools to deepen our awareness to heal our wounds, and embrace being a badass in every area of our lives.

With her direct but extremely nurturing approach, McKay encourages others to live happier and more fulfilling lives with a clear sense of purpose, infused with a resilient and playful spirit.

Kate is the author of the international best-selling book Claim Your Inner Badass, Claim Your Inner Peace- a daily journal and has been a columnist for numerous years. She has written for Entrepreneur, appeared on numerous national and local radio, podcasts and tv, including PBS. Kate has been interviewed and appeared in several magazines and newspaper articles.

Check out Kate's podcast: Master Your Life with Kate McKay

Kate resides in Saint Petersburg, Florida.

How Can You Help?

Thank You For Reading My Book!

I really appreciate all of your feedback, and I love hearing what you have to say.

amazon.com/author/katemckay

Please leave me an honest review on Amazon letting me know what you thought of the book.

Thanks so much!

Kate McKay

High-Performance Coach

How To Work With Kate McKay,
High-Performance Coach?

Want more information on how you can hire Kate to Speak at your event or work with her one-on-one as your Coach?

Click here: Work With Kate

Visit Kate's website: www.kate-mckay.com

Follow Kate McKay:

Facebook: https://www.facebook.com/iamkatemckay

Twitter:

https://twitter.com/Katemckay18

Linked In:

linkedin.com/in/katemckaycoach

Instagram:

https://www.instagram.com/iamkatemckay